Macmillan/McGraw-Hill READING

Contributors

The Princeton Review, Time Magazine, Accelerated Reader

The Princeton Review is not
affiliated with Princeton
University or ETS.

learning through listening

Students with print disabilities may be eligible to obtain an accessible, audio version
of the pupil edition of this textbook. Please call Recording for the Blind & Dyslexic at
1-800-221-4792 for complete information.

Macmillan/McGraw-Hill

*A Division of The **McGraw·Hill** Companies*

Published by Macmillan/McGraw-Hill, a division of The McGraw-Hill Companies, Inc., Two Penn Plaza, NY, NY 10121

Printed in the United States of America

ISBN 0-02-188566-4/2, Bk.1
4 5 6 7 8 9 110/043 04 03 02

Macmillan/McGraw-Hill READING

Authors

James Flood

Jan E. Hasbrouck

James V. Hoffman

Diane Lapp

Donna Lubcker

Angela Shelf Medearis

Scott Paris

Steven Stahl

Josefina Villamil Tinajero

Karen D. Wood

Macmillan
McGraw-Hill

New York   Farmington

UNIT 1

What's New?

UNIT 2

Just Between Us

UNIT 3

Express Yourself

9

What's New

Morning Song

Today is a day to catch tadpoles.
Today is a day to explore.
Today is a day to get started.
Come on! Let's not sleep anymore.

Outside the sunbeams are dancing.
The leaves sing a rustling song.
Today is a day for adventures,
and I hope that you'll come along!

by Bobbi Katz

12

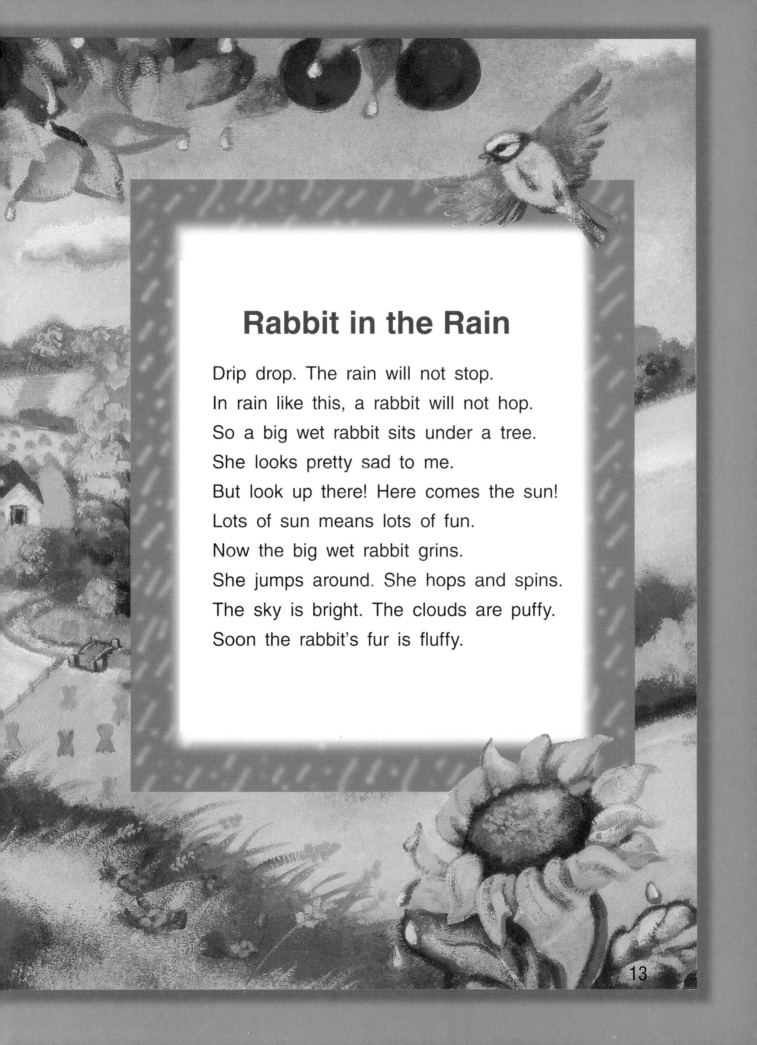

Rabbit in the Rain

Drip drop. The rain will not stop.
In rain like this, a rabbit will not hop.
So a big wet rabbit sits under a tree.
She looks pretty sad to me.
But look up there! Here comes the sun!
Lots of sun means lots of fun.
Now the big wet rabbit grins.
She jumps around. She hops and spins.
The sky is bright. The clouds are puffy.
Soon the rabbit's fur is fluffy.

Meet Constance Andrea Keremes

When Constance Andrea Keremes was a little girl, she pretended to be famous people, animals, and even space aliens. She also made up stories and rhymes. Even as a grown-up, Keremes still likes to pretend. This has helped her to write several poems and stories which have been published. "A story or poem can bring to life all the magical ideas that you have in your head," she says.

Meet Dorothy Donohue

Dorothy Donohue loves animals. For nine years, she had a pet rabbit of her own named Claire. "She would eat my golden retriever's food and only let him eat after she was finished. She was quite a rabbit." Ms. Donohue is the illustrator of several children's books, including *Big Little on the Farm*, *Believing Sophie*, and *Maybe Yes, Maybe No, Maybe Maybe*.

14

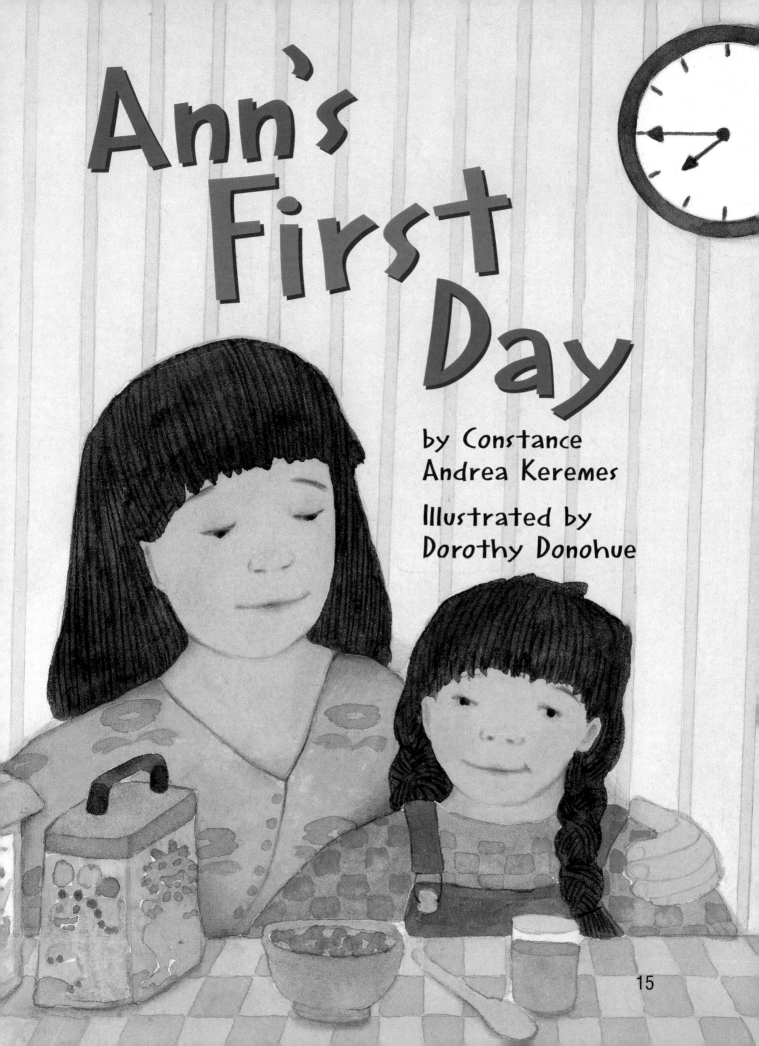

Ann's First Day

by Constance
Andrea Keremes

Illustrated by
Dorothy Donohue

15

Today is the first day of school.
Robert runs. Jill jumps. Matt marches.
Stephanie skips.

Ann does not move at all.

"Hurry, Ann!" says Mom. "You will be late for school."

Ann still does not budge. She is scared. She has never been to this school before. Her family moved to this town two months ago.

Last year at her old school, she knew
all the boys and girls.

There were Luis and Lonnie, Marcus
and Maria, and Jenny and James.

But best of all there was Robbie. Robbie was the class pet. He was a fluffy white rabbit with a nose as pink as a peppermint. When Ann learned she would move away at the end of the school year, the class decided that she could take Robbie with her.

Ever since Ann moved, she has been spending all her time with Robbie. They play games. They share snacks. They do everything together. Robbie is not just a pet. He is a friend.

"I wish that Robbie could come to school with me," she says.

"I don't think rabbits like homework," says Mom with a serious face. "Robbie will be happy to stay at home eating carrots until you come back. Now hurry up. We are going to be the last ones there."

But Ann and Mom are not the last ones.
Someone else is going to school, too. Robbie.

After Ann and Mom leave for school,
Robbie pops out of his cage and follows them.

Now Ann is at school. Mom kisses her good-bye.

Ann slowly walks into her classroom. All the other boys and girls are already sitting at their desks. Ann feels shy.

Each desk has a special card with a child's name on it. Ann looks left. She looks right. She cannot find her name!

Someone named Carlos laughs. Then someone named Jessica laughs and points at Ann's feet. Ann feels awful. She wriggles her toes. Did she forget her shoes? She takes a peek down.

And there between her feet is something as pink as a peppermint. A nose! Robbie's nose!

"Robbie!" laughs Ann. "What are you doing here?"

"It looks like somebody has followed you to school," says the teacher, Mr. Garcia. He has a nice smile. Ann smiles back.

"Robbie was the class pet in my old school," she says.

"Now he is my pet."

27

"A pet rabbit!" says one boy. "You're lucky!"

"I have a turtle at home," says Jessica. "He crawls."

All the children crowd around to meet Robbie. Robbie is very happy. He wriggles his nose. The boys and girls clap. Then he wriggles his ears. The boys and girls clap even louder.

Then Robbie hops his highest hop and flicks his fluffy tail. The boys and girls clap loudest of all.

Robbie feels right at home in school.
He rubs his soft pink nose against
Ann's hands. Ann smiles. Now she feels
right at home, too.

Story Questions & Activities

1 Why is Ann afraid to go to school?

2 Why is Robbie special to Ann?

3 Do you think Ann will make friends at her new school? Tell why you think so.

4 What is this story about?

5 In some stories, animals go places they might not go in real life. In "Make Way for Ducklings" a family of ducks goes all over the city looking for a place to live. How is Robbie the Rabbit like the Mallard family?

Write a Personal Narrative

Write about your first day of school. What was it like? How did you feel? What did you do? Tell about your day in the order things happened.

Make a Pet Book

There are many different kinds of pets. Some people like cats and dogs. Others like birds, rabbits, fish, or mice. Choose a pet that you would like to have. Draw a picture of the pet. Put your pictures together with your classmates to make a pet book.

Make a Class Guide

What would a new boy or girl need to know about your class? Make a guide that would help a new classmate. Include classmates' names, the daily schedule, and anything else that might be helpful.

Find Out More

Find out how to take care of a pet rabbit. What does it like to eat? Where would it sleep? Are there any special things you would do for the pet? Make a poster that tells about caring for your pet.

Using Parts of a Book

A title page tells the name of the book and author.
Some books have a contents page. It tells what
chapters are in the book and on what pages they start.

Henry and Mudge
UNDER THE
Yellow Moon

The Fourth Book of Their Adventures

Story by Cynthia Rylant
Pictures by Suçie Stevenson

Contents

Together in the Fall   5
Under the Yellow Moon   13
Thanksgiving Guest   35

Use the pages above to answer the questions.

1 What is the title of the book? *underlined*

2 Who is the author of the book? *circled*

3 On what page in the book can you start reading
a chapter called "Thanksgiving Guest"? *pg. 35*

4 Pretend you are writing a book. Think of a title.
Make up a title page for your own book. *Ruby
the frustfull Rabbit*

34

TEST POWER

Always read the directions carefully before you read the story.

DIRECTIONS:
Read the story. Then read each question about the story.

SAMPLE

Sister Learns How

Peter's sister wanted to play baseball. She asked him to go with her to the ball field. Peter gave his sister a mitt. He showed her how to hold it.

Peter threw the ball. His sister caught it. Peter's sister liked baseball. She wanted to learn more. Peter showed her how to hit the ball. Peter threw the ball. His sister hit it. Peter told her to run, but she didn't know where to go. Peter showed her where to go. He showed her all the bases.

Peter threw the ball again. His sister swung the bat and hit the ball. She ran around the bases. She made a home run.

Peter cheered. His sister was a great baseball player.

1 Where do Peter and his sister play ball?
  ○ Peter's yard
  ● The ball field
  ○ At a friend's house

2 What will Peter's sister say the next time Peter asks her to play ball?
  ● Yes, it is fun.
  ○ No thank you, it's boring.
  ○ Yes, but I don't know how.

My Dog Jake

I take my dog outside with me,
Jake likes to play a game, you see.

I throw my ball
And then I call,
Run, Jake!
We have a race.
We run a mile,
We then run home.

Every day it's just the same,
Jake and I play our game.

Meet Cynthia Rylant

Cynthia Rylant says, "The idea for Henry and Mudge came from my own life. I once owned a 200-pound English mastiff named Mudge. My son, Nate, was seven years old at the time. The two together became Henry and Mudge in my books.

"Anyone who's ever loved a dog knows what a treasure a good dog is. You just can't be unhappy for very long when you have a good dog licking your face, shaking your hand, and drooling all over your shoes."

Meet Suçie Stevenson

Suçie Stevenson loves to draw pictures for the stories about Henry and Mudge. She says: "The stories are about things that have happened to me."

When asked if she had anything to tell children who might like to be artists, Ms. Stevenson said: "Don't listen to what others tell you to draw. Put colors where you want them. Just start drawing."

Henry and Mudge

Story by Cynthia Rylant
Pictures by Suçie Stevenson

HENRY

Henry had no brothers
and no sisters.
"I want a brother,"
he told his parents.
"Sorry," they said.
Henry had no friends
on his street.

"I want to live
on a different street,"
he told his parents.
"Sorry," they said.
Henry had no pets
at home.
"I want to have a dog,"
he told his parents.
"Sorry," they *almost* said.

But first they looked
at their house
with no brothers and sisters.
Then they looked
at their street
with no children.
Then they looked
at Henry's face.

Then they looked at each other.
"Okay," they said.
"I want to hug you!"
Henry told his parents.
And he did.

Mudge

Henry searched for a dog.

"Not just any dog," said Henry.

"Not a short one," he said.

"Not a curly one," he said.

"And no pointed ears."

Then he found Mudge.
Mudge had floppy ears,
not pointed.
And Mudge had straight fur,
not curly.
But Mudge was short.
"Because he's a puppy,"
Henry said.
"He'll grow."

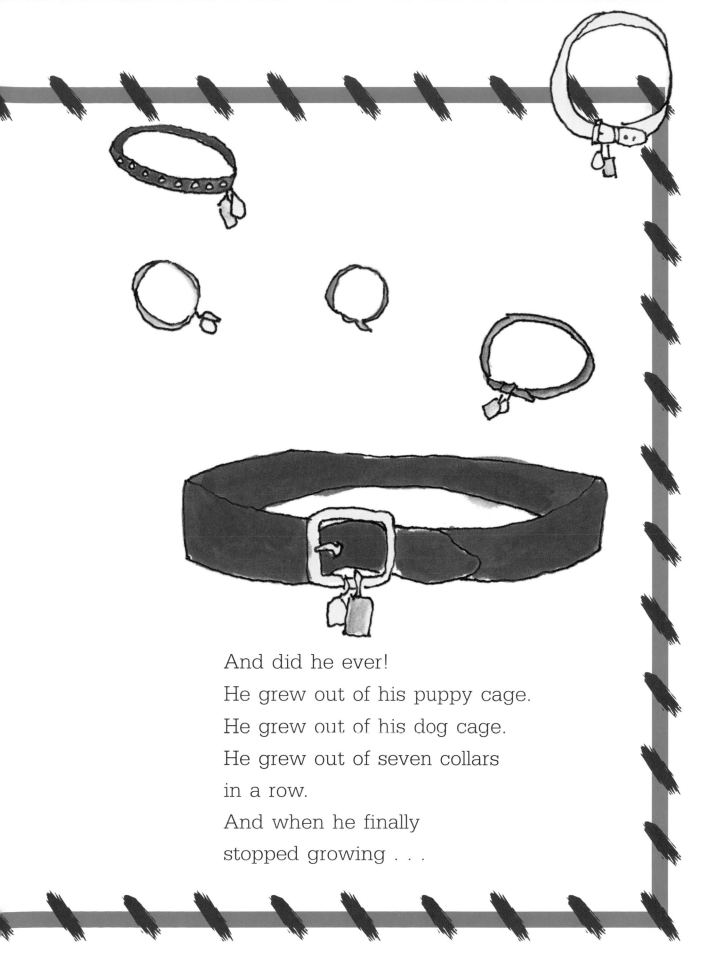

And did he ever!
He grew out of his puppy cage.
He grew out of his dog cage.
He grew out of seven collars
in a row.
And when he finally
stopped growing . . .

he weighed one hundred eighty pounds,
he stood three feet tall,
and he drooled.
"I'm glad you're not short,"
Henry said.

And Mudge licked him,
then sat on him.

Henry

Henry used to walk
to school alone.
When he walked
he used to worry about
tornadoes,
ghosts,
biting dogs,
and bullies.

He walked as fast
as he could.
He looked straight ahead.
He never looked back.
But now he walked to school
with Mudge.

And now when he walked,
he thought about
vanilla ice cream,
rain,
rocks,
and good dreams.
He walked to school
but not too fast.
He walked to school
and sometimes backward.

He walked to school
and patted Mudge's big head,
happy.

Story Questions & Activities

1 Who is the main character?

2 How does Mudge help Henry?

3 Suppose Henry got another dog. What would the dog be like? Tell why you think so.

4 What is this story about?

5 How are Ann and her pet rabbit Robbie like Henry and Mudge?

Write a Story

Write a story about someone you like as much as Henry likes Mudge. Think about a time you spent together. Tell what happens from beginning to end. Tell about your feelings.

How Big Is Big?

Do you know of an animal that is bigger or weighs more than Mudge? Draw a picture of it.

Going Home from School

Henry and Mudge walk home from school every day. How do you come home from school? Make a map that shows how you go. Write the names of streets you take.

Find Out More

Henry wanted a dog that was tall, with straight fur and floppy ears. If you could choose any kind of pet, what would you want it to look like? Make a list. Find out what kind of pet matches your list.

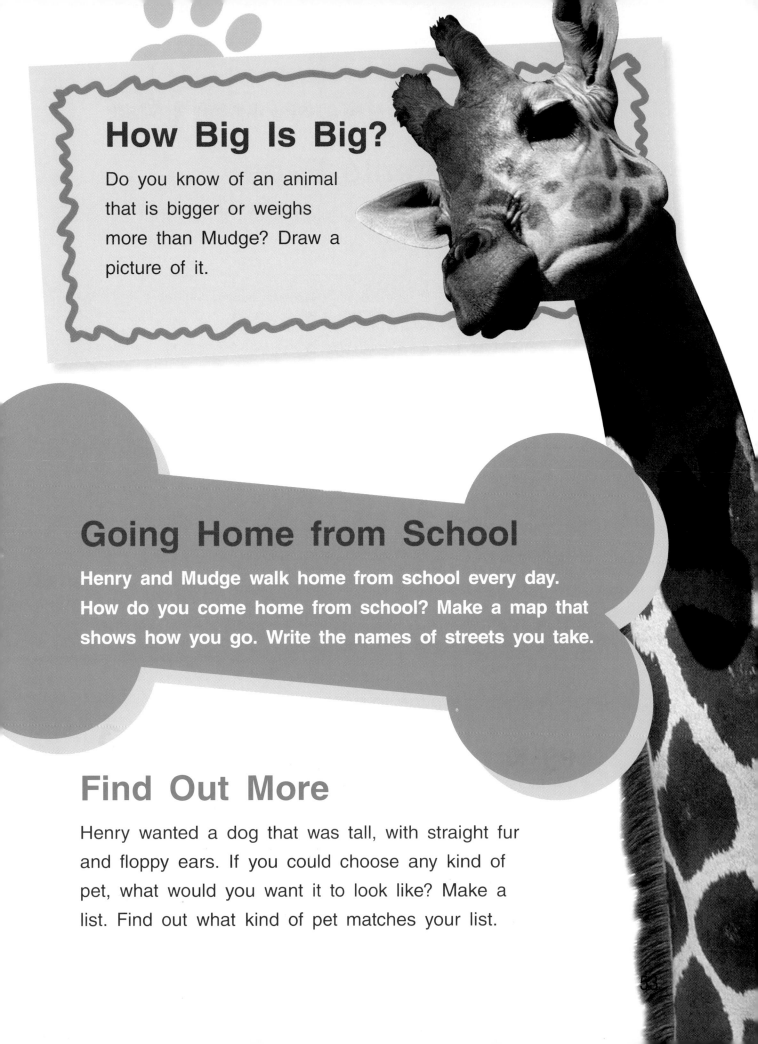

Use a Contents Page

The table of contents tells you information about what is inside the book.

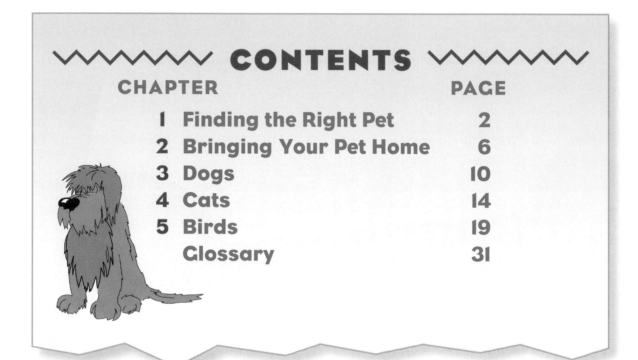

CONTENTS

CHAPTER		PAGE
1	Finding the Right Pet	2
2	Bringing Your Pet Home	6
3	Dogs	10
4	Cats	14
5	Birds	19
	Glossary	31

Use the contents page to answer the questions.

1. What chapter should you read to learn about dogs? **3** **pg. 10**

2. What is Chapter 5 about? **Birds**

3. What part of the book is different from the other parts? How do you know? **glossary it shows meanings**

4. How does the contents page help you? **find the thing I'm looking for**

TEST POWER

Read the story carefully before you answer the questions.

DIRECTIONS:
Read the story. Then read each question about the story.

SAMPLE

What Does Brenda Do?

My sister's name is Brenda. She was fifteen when I was born. Brenda is a geologist. Geologists study the Earth. They study rocks and volcanoes. Brenda studies metals. She mostly studies copper. Copper is a metal found in the Earth. Arizona and New Mexico are places with lots of copper. Copper is used to make many things. It is often used to make wire and pipes.

Yesterday, I went to work with Brenda. I saw her maps. I saw the tools that she uses to find copper. It was an interesting day. When I grow up, I might be a geologist, too.

1 What is a FACT from this story?
- ○ Copper comes from plants.
- ◉ Copper is a metal.
- ○ Copper is a food.

2 How does the author feel about her sister's job?
- ◉ She thinks it is interesting.
- ○ She thinks it is too hard.
- ○ She thinks it is confusing.

The Green Field

Grandma and I went out one day.
In a field we stopped to play.
We sat beneath a big green tree,
Where we surprised a yellow bee!
We saw flowers,
We saw seeds,
We even saw some plain old weeds.
My grandma and I have so much fun,
Playing in the summer sun.

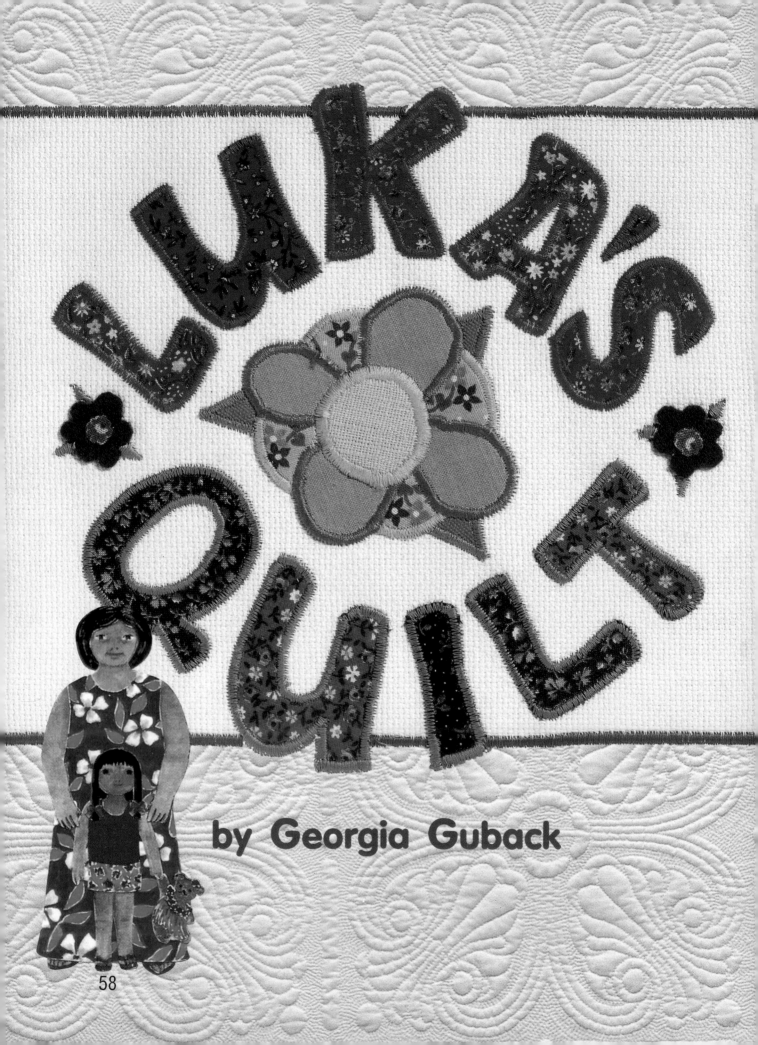

LUKA'S QUILT

by Georgia Guback

My tutu lives with us. Tutu. That's Hawaiian for grandmother. Tutu takes care of me while Mom and Dad work. We do lots of things together. I like that, and so does Tutu. But all that changed when the quilt came along.

One morning Tutu said, "I had a dream last night. I dreamed I was in a beautiful garden. There were flowers everywhere. It gave me an idea for a quilt. This quilt will be for you, Luka. I made a quilt for your mom. Now it's your turn."

"Will it have flowers on it?" I asked.

"Oh yes," Tutu replied. "It's a flower garden. There will be all kinds of flowers."

"It's going to be so pretty," I said.

"It will take a long time to make," said Tutu. "You'll have to be patient."

"That's okay," I said. "I can help."

After breakfast Tutu and I went to the fabric store.

"Choose a color," said Tutu.

There were so many pretty colors.

"I like that yellow," I said. "And that pink. And some of that blue. And the lavender. And this orange is nice."

Tutu laughed. "Not so fast," she said. "Choose one color. Just one."

"How can it be a flower garden if there's just one color?" I asked.

"You'll see," said Tutu.

Just one color! Green. I chose green because flowers have green leaves. The flower colors would come later.

Tutu sketched and cut and pinned and basted. And
I got to help. This quilt is going to be so pretty, I kept
thinking. I could hardly wait for the flowers.

At last Tutu put the quilt on the quilting frame. "Serious
work now," she said. And I knew I wasn't big enough to
help anymore.

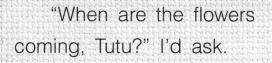

"When are the flowers coming, Tutu?" I'd ask.

She'd smile and answer, "You'll see, Luka. You'll see."

Then one day a long time after, Tutu took the quilt off the frame. She ironed it and put it on my bed. "For you, Luka," she said.

The flowers! There were no flowers! "Where are the flowers?" I cried.

"Here," said Tutu. "See, here's amaryllis. And here's ginger. And over there is jacaranda."

"Everything's white," I said. "How can there be flowers with no pretty flower colors?"

"This is the way we make our quilts," said Tutu. "Two colors. It's our Island tradition. You chose green, remember?"

"I thought the green was for leaves," I cried. "All the flowers in our garden are in colors. It can't be a flower garden if the flowers are white."

Tutu's eyes got watery, and she quietly turned and went to her room and shut the door.

I looked at Tutu's quilt again. I thought it was going to be so pretty, and all it was was white.

I sat down and cried.

Things changed after that. Tutu and I used to be such good friends. Now we had nothing to say to each other. We didn't do things together anymore. And all because of that quilt. It's going to stay like this forever, I thought. It was awful.

But Tutu surprised me. A few days later she said, "Today is Lei Day. You've never been to a Lei Day celebration, Luka. Let's declare a truce and see what's going on at the park."

"What's a truce?" I asked.

"That's when people put aside their differences and come together again for a little while," Tutu answered.

I didn't see how that was going to work, but it was worth a try.

"Okay," I said.

I filled the water jug, and Tutu got the tatami mat, and we stopped at Aiko's to buy bento for our picnic. By the time the bus came, it was almost beginning to feel like old times.

There was so much going on at the park. We listened to the music. We watched the dancing. We spread our mat under a tree and ate our bento. And Tutu treated me to shave ice.

Later we came to a place where kids were making leis.

"Come," said a lady. "Make a lei."

"Is it okay, Tutu?" I asked.

"Go ahead," said Tutu.

The lady got me started. She gave me a long needle and strong thread and showed me how to string the flowers together.

There were all kinds of blossoms. They were in cardboard boxes with wet newspapers all around to keep them fresh. I chose a pink flower. Next I added a yellow. Then an orange. And then a lavender. Tutu laughed. "No, not that way, Luka," she said. "Choose one color, maybe two. But no more than two."

I could feel myself getting angry, and I tried not to. I was remembering our truce.

"Tutu," I said, "it's my lei."

"But . . . ," Tutu began. Then she stopped. She was remembering our truce, too, and she didn't say another word.

Things got better at once. I didn't feel angry anymore, and I made my lei my way. It turned out very pretty, and I got to keep it and wear it home.

So the truce worked, and I felt happy. "I'm glad you had that truce idea, Tutu," I said. "I had a good time."

"So did I," Tutu answered.

By bedtime the happy feeling was still with me. I looked at Tutu's quilt again. Maybe a white flower garden wasn't so bad. I snuggled underneath her quilt and fell asleep.

The next day
Tutu said, "Luka,
I was looking at
your lei last night.
I saw your flower
garden in it, and it
gave me an idea."

I got to help with Tutu's idea. I chose pretty flower colors from her scrap baskets, and then I helped sketch and cut and baste. Then Tutu did the sewing and quilting.

A long time later, after my pretty flower lei had dried out and turned brown, Tutu called me. We went to my bedroom. And there they were—like magic! All the flowers I had dreamed of in a special quilted lei!

"Just for you, Luka," said Tutu. "Now you have all your flowers and all your colors."

"Oh, it's so pretty!" I cried.

And all at once I was hugging Tutu and she was hugging me back. And everything was better again.

I like my quilt a lot now. Sometimes I have it plain—
my white flower garden. And sometimes I put Tutu's quilted
lei on top and have my flower garden in color. I like it both
ways. But what I like most is that Tutu and I are friends
again. And I can tell Tutu likes that best of all, too.

MEET
Georgia Guback

Georgia Guback got the idea for *Luka's Quilt* after she saw a Hawaiian quilt. She liked the quilt so much she decided to find out more about Hawaii. She used the facts she learned to write the book.

"I like to communicate with young children. I hope my books help children see that they can find answers to problems," she says. She plans to write many more children's books.

Story Questions & Activities

1. What colors are in Luka's quilt?

2. Why do Luka and Tutu stop talking to each other?

3. Why is it important for Luka and Tutu to forget about their fight for a while?

4. What is this story mostly about?

5. If Luka were the new girl in Ann's class, what might she bring to school to show her classmates?

Write a Letter

Write a letter to a friend. Tell your friend about a time you spent with a relative. It could be a funny thing that happened or a problem you solved together. Tell what happened in order from beginning to end.

Celebrations

Luka and Tutu attend a Lei Day celebration. What are some special days you like? Birthday parties? Weddings? A certain holiday? Design a sign that announces your special event.

Make a Paper Lei

Materials: string, scissors, tissue paper, tape

1. Cut a long piece of string or yarn.
2. Use scissors to cut tissue paper into squares.
3. Pinch and twist the center of one square.
4. Wrap the tip of the twisted end in clear tape.
5. With a pencil, poke a hole in the flower's center.
6. Thread your string through the hole in the flower.
7. Make and string more flowers until your lei is finished.

Find Out More

Tutu stitches jacaranda, amaryllis, and ginger flowers into Luka's quilt. What do these flowers look like? Find pictures of these and other flowers that grow in Hawaii and draw them. Write the name of each flower under its picture.

STUDY SKILLS

Read a Glossary

A glossary is like a dictionary. It tells you the meaning of a word and how to say the word aloud. The guide words show you what page the word is on.

Gg   garden / graze

garden   A place where people grow flowers or vegetables. When our cousins visit, they always bring us fresh tomatoes from their *garden*.
gar•den (GAHR duhn) *noun, plural* **gardens**.

grandmother   Your father's mother or your mother's mother. My *grandmother* lives in New York City.
grand•moth•er (GRAND muthh uhr) *noun, plural* **grandmothers**.

Use the glossary to answer the questions.

1 What does the word *grandmother* mean? ~~You~~ underlined
    under lined

2 What shows you how to pronounce *garden*? underlined
    (Gahrduhn)

3 Find the glossary at the back of your reader. Look at the order of the words. How are they arranged?
    abc order

4 Which word do you think might be the last entry on the glossary page above? garden

TEST POWER

Which words in the story tell you about feelings?

DIRECTIONS:

Read the story. Then read each question about the story.

SAMPLE

Sally's New Bike

Sally got a red bicycle for her birthday. She was very excited. She wanted to learn to ride. Her father told her that he could teach her. "Learning to ride takes practice," he said.

"I know," Sally replied. "I'm ready to learn." The sun was shining brightly. Sally did not care that it was hot.

She sat on her new bike. She was a little nervous. At first, her father held the bicycle for her.

Sally fell once or twice. But each time, she got back on her bike. After three days of practice, Sally could ride all by herself!

1 How did Sally feel when she received her birthday present?
○ Nervous
● Happy
○ Angry

2 When does this story take place?
○ On a rainy day
● On a sunny day
○ At night

My Goat Tom

My horse Joe likes to eat oats;
My pig Sam likes to eat toast.
My dog Moe likes meat loaf and beans;
My cat Tess likes a touch of light cream.
My goat Tom eats plastic and soap,
Wet socks, dry coats, long yellow rope,
All kinds of buttons, bicycles, and boots,
Pens, tin cans, and then for a drink
He drinks right out of our kitchen sink!

Meet Angela Shelf Medearis

As a child, Angela Shelf Medearis loved to read. At the age of thirty, she began to write her own books. "I want to write the kind of books I always longed to find in the library when I was a child," she says. Now her talent and humor have made Medearis one of Texas's most popular children's book authors.

Meet Karen Chandler

Karen Chandler uses computers to do her artwork. For *The Roundup at Rio Ranch*, she mixed photos with illustrations in a computer program called PhotoShop. Ms. Chandler is also the illustrator of *The Keeper of the Swamp*.

The Roundup at Rio Ranch

By Angela Shelf Medearis
Illustrated by Karen Chandler

"José," my brother Antonio yells. "Wake up! Today you are going with us on the roundup."

I jump out of bed and pull on my blue jeans and boots. I've been waiting a long time to go on a cattle roundup.

The sun is coming up, but it is still cool outside. I shiver a little. We are going to count the cows in the back pasture. Papa likes to start working before it gets too hot.

I put on my hat and tie a red bandanna around my neck. My grandfather smiles at me.

"You look like a real *vaquero*, a real little cowboy," Grandfather says. He has told me all about the Spanish soldiers who brought herds of cattle from Spain to Texas in the 1800s. As the herds grew bigger, the soldiers became *vaqueros*, or cowboys. *Vaca* is the Spanish word for cow.

"Do you want to ride in the truck with me?" Grandfather asks.

"No, thanks. I want to ride my horse," I say.

Papa, Antonio, and I saddle our horses. Papa helps me put my western saddle on Sugar. A western saddle is really comfortable. It's got a large seat and a saddle horn so that cowboys can tie their lariats to it.

Sugar nudges me with her head. She is a mustang. Mustangs are small, tough, and hardworking. They were brought to Texas by the Spanish soldiers who became cowboys. Mustangs are good at rounding up cattle.

"Here is your lariat, José," Papa says. "It is the same one I used when I was your age."

"Thank you, Papa," I say and give him a hug. The lariat is a long, nylon rope. It has a loop on one end. I try to throw the loop around the fence post, but it lands around Antonio instead.

"Moo," Antonio yells. He laughs and paws the ground with his boot.

"Just keep trying," Grandfather says.

We ride toward the back pasture. Sam and Sis, our cow dogs, run after us. They help us round up the cattle.

It is very hot and dusty. We carefully check the barbed wire fence as we ride along. I help Papa and Antonio fix a broken post. We use a post-hole digger, called a *poseda* in Spanish, to dig a new hole. Then we string barbed wire between the posts to keep the cattle from running away.

The roar of a helicopter comes toward us. I look up and wave at the pilot as he flies over us. We use the helicopter to help us count the cows that hide in the deep brush.

We ride into the back pasture and start rounding up the cows. The dogs bark and nip at the cows' heels. Grandfather drives around and around. He uses the truck to herd the cattle toward us. Papa and Antonio rope the cows with their lariats and move them into the corral. I whistle, yell, and swing my lariat. I keep missing the cows.

"Just keep trying," Grandfather shouts from the truck.

Papa and Antonio count the cows and calves. They check their ear tags to make sure all of the cows belong to us. They inspect them to see if they are healthy.

The cows need to be moved from the back pasture to the one on the east side. They have eaten most of the grass in the back pasture. Luckily, there is plenty of grass in the east pasture. After we move the cows, we put out big blocks of salt. The cows crowd around the salt, licking it with their long, pink tongues. Next, we check the water in the tanks to make sure the cows have enough.

Finally, we are done and it's time to go home. Papa and Antonio ride ahead of me. Sugar cannot canter as fast as their horses. Soon, I am far behind. Dust covers my face. It gets into my eyes and nose. I slow down to a walk and wipe my face with my bandanna.

"Wait for me," I yell. But they are too far away to hear me. Sugar and I are too little to keep up with Papa and Antonio. "We'll be fine," I say, patting Sugar's neck.

Suddenly, I hear a funny noise. I stop to look. Something is tangled up in the bushes at the bottom of the hill. It is a small, brown calf. The hill is too steep for me to climb down. I try to figure out what I should do. There is no one around to help me.

I gently swing my lariat through the air. It lands near the calf. I roll it up and try again and again. Finally, the loop lands around the calf's foot. I pull the loop closed with a yank. The calf slides out of the bushes, crying. I loop the rope around the saddle horn.

"Get up there, Sugar," I say. Sugar pulls the calf up the hill. "Easy now, girl. Whoa."

Sugar stands still and the calf pulls against the rope, trying to get away. I walk toward it, softly singing a little song. I gently check the calf to see if it is hurt. There are some deep scratches on its left leg. Taking the medicine out of my saddlebag, I put it on the scratches.

Just then, Grandfather drives up in the truck. He looks pleased when he sees the calf.

"Good work, José!" Grandfather calls to me. "Only a true cowboy can spot a calf in the brush, rope it, and pull it to safety."

I smile at Grandfather as I take my lariat off the calf. It shakes its head and trots off.

"Rounding up cattle is hard work. Let's go eat," Grandfather says.

"And after dinner, you can tell me more stories about the *vaqueros*," I say, grinning. Sugar neighs happily as we follow Grandfather's truck home.

Story Questions & Activities

1 Where does this story take place?

2 Why is the setting important to the story?

3 Why do you think José wants to be like a real cowboy?

4 What is this story mainly about?

5 How are José and his grandfather like Luka and her grandmother? How are they different?

Write a Story About a Place

José lives on a ranch. Write a story about the place where you live, or a place where you would like to live. Show what it's like to live there. Tell about what happens in one day at that place. Make sure you include a beginning, a middle, and an end to your story.

Draw a Map of Rio Ranch

José helps round up the cows and move them from the back pasture into the corral. Use the description in the story to draw a map of Rio Ranch. Remember to include the ranch house, the corral, the back pasture, and the fence.

Sing a Cowboy Song

Cowboys and cowgirls used to sing songs around a campfire at night. "Home on the Range" is a favorite cowboy song. Use José's story to make up your own cowboy song. You can use the tune of "Home on the Range."

Find Out More

A Texas longhorn is a kind of cow that is often found on a ranch. What is special about the longhorn? What makes it different from other cows?

111

Use an Index

Suppose you wanted to learn some facts about life on a ranch, but you didn't want to read a whole book about it. You could use the index of a book to find where to look for the information.

·········· INDEX ··········

bandanna, 13

barbed wire, 7–8

brush, 2, 5

calf, 4–7

canter, 11

cattle, 2–3, 18–20

corral, 4

cowboy, 5–7, 9

herd, 1, 3–4

lariat, 6

mustang, 8–10

pasture, 2

ranch, 12–14

saddle, 16–17, 21

Use the index to answer the questions.

1 On what pages can you find out about cowboys?

5-7,9

2 What can you read about on pages 12, 13, and 14?

ranches

3 How are the words in an index ordered?

abc order

4 Words that begin with some letters of the alphabet are missing from this index. Which letters of the alphabet are missing? *A,d,e,f,g,i,j,k,n,o,q,t,u,v,w,x,y,z*

TEST POWER

Look for clues in the story that tell you about feelings.

DIRECTIONS:
Read the story. Then read each question about the story.

SAMPLE

Going to the City

For my birthday, I went to the city. I had never been there before. I didn't know if I would like it. It was a long drive, and I fell asleep before we were even halfway there. When I woke up, there were tall buildings everywhere.

I looked out the window. I had never seen so many people. Where did they all come from? Did they all live in the city? I looked at all the stores. I saw a candy store. I asked if we could stop so I could buy some candy. My mother said, "Maybe later."

We spent most of the day exploring. We looked in lots of shops. I went back to the candy store and bought some candy. I had a great day in the city.

1 How does the author feel about candy?
- ● He likes it.
- ○ He doesn't like it.
- ○ It hurts his teeth.

2 What will the author of this story say when he is asked about the city?
- ● It is a good place to visit.
- ○ It has too many people.
- ○ There are no candy stores.

When We Think of the Past

We remember the years
That pile up like snow.
We remember the tears
That we cried long ago.
We remember the trails
Where we said good-bye.
We remember the tales
That tell us why.

Welcome to
a New Museum

The Charles H. Wright Museum
of African American History

A Visit to a Special Place

When Katrina and Frederick Jones go to the Charles H. Wright Museum of African American History, they can see themselves. The Detroit, Michigan, museum is all about black Americans. It is the biggest African American history museum anywhere. And Katrina and Frederick, who are brother and sister, are in a museum show. Molds of the two kids were used to make statues. The statues show Africans on a model of a slave boat.

These statues show what life was like for Africans on a slave boat.

FELICIA HUNT-TAYLOR

RIGHT AND COVER: PETER YATES/SABA; INSET: MCGRAW HILL SCHOOL PUBLISHING

Frederick and Katrina Jones were models for the statues.

117

You can hear the music of famous singing groups.

The Top Five

Girls and boys love to see these things at the museum.

1. A room where you can hear African American music
2. The first traffic light
3. Mae Jemison's space suit
4. The model of a slave boat
5. The floor of the big room you first walk into (see page 116)

It took a long time for artists to make the molds. First, they coated the children's bodies with oil. Then, the artists covered them with paper. The paper was wet and sticky. Soon it dried and got hard. "I couldn't move for over an hour. And I couldn't talk. Moving or talking would have cracked the mold," Katrina said.

Mae Jemison's space suit is at the museum. She was the first African American woman in space.

"Seeing myself is kind of fun," says Frederick. When Frederick grows up, he wants to show his children the boat. Then he can say, "That's me!"

When people visit the museum, they see flags flying. Each stands for a place where Africans were once taken to be slaves.

Inside, people see the names of 60 great Africans and African Americans. People can also see things that were thought up by African Americans.

A golf tee and the first design for a dime are two of the things you can see at the museum. It's a place with many surprises!

LEFT AND TOP LEFT: PETER YATES/SABA. MAE JEMISON, NASA

People can see the history of the civil rights movement in the U.S.

MICHIGAN

Detroit

FIND OUT MORE
Visit our website:
www.mhschool.com/reading

*inter*NET
CONNECTION

The museum is in Detroit, Michigan.

1 In what part of the museum are the statues of Katrina and Frederick?

2 Why is Mae Jemison's space suit in the museum?

3 Why was the Charles H. Wright Museum created?

4 What is the main idea of this selection?

5 When Tutu makes a quilt, she is passing on part of her history and culture to Luka. How do Katrina and Frederick share their history and culture?

Write a Personal Narrative

Write about your visit to a museum or another famous place. Tell about what you saw and learned. What was your favorite part? What made it special to you?

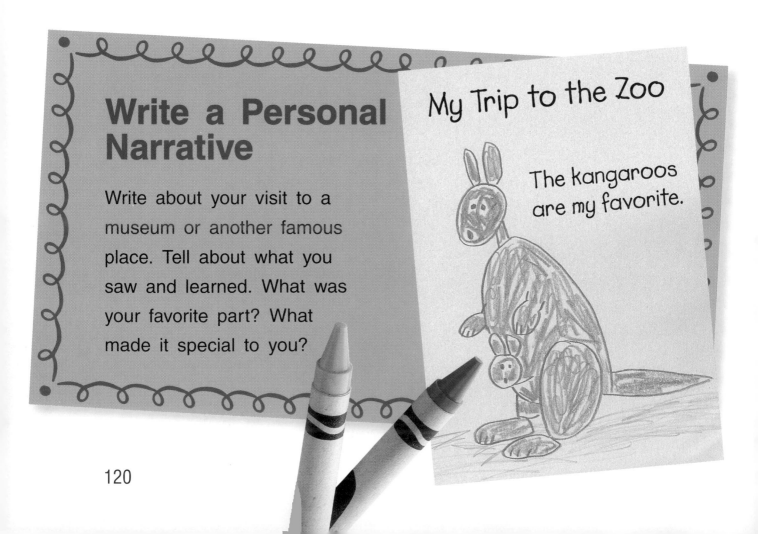

My Trip to the Zoo

The kangaroos are my favorite.

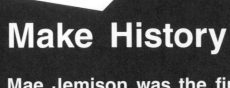

Make History

Mae Jemison was the first African American woman astronaut. How would you like to make history? Make a history book page about yourself. Include a drawing of yourself and explain what you did to be a part of history.

Write a Poem About Freedom

Write a poem about freedom that tells what you think it means to be free. Use words that show how you feel.

Find Out More

George Washington Carver is one of the most famous African American inventors. Find out more about his discoveries.

Using the Internet

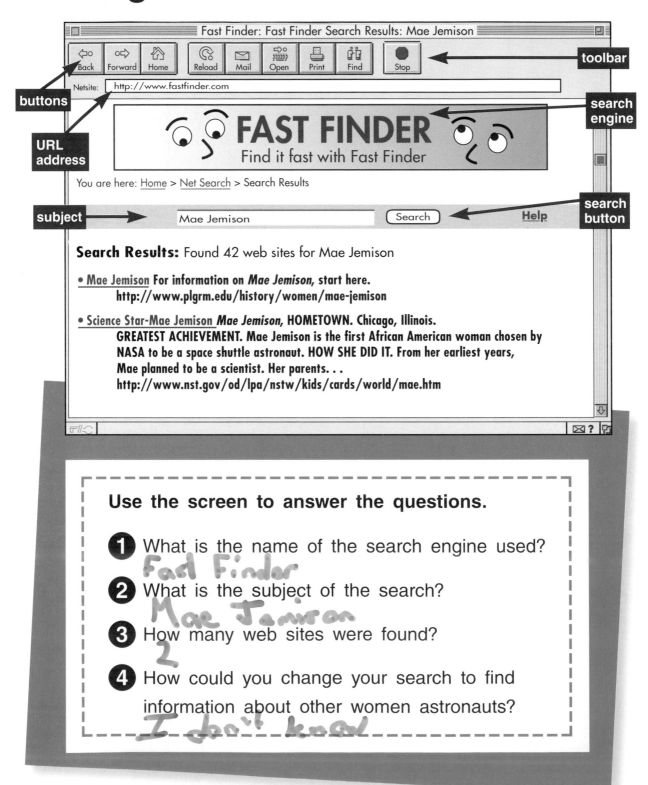

	Fast Finder: Fast Finder Search Results: Mae Jemison	

toolbar

Back Forward Home Reload Mail Open Print Find Stop

buttons

Netsite: http://www.fastfinder.com

URL address

search engine

FAST FINDER
Find it fast with Fast Finder

You are here: Home > Net Search > Search Results

subject

Mae Jemison   Search   Help

search button

Search Results: Found 42 web sites for Mae Jemison

• Mae Jemison **For information on** *Mae Jemison,* **start here.**
    http://www.plgrm.edu/history/women/mae-jemison

• Science Star-Mae Jemison *Mae Jemison,* **HOMETOWN. Chicago, Illinois.**
    GREATEST ACHIEVEMENT. Mae Jemison is the first African American woman chosen by
    NASA to be a space shuttle astronaut. HOW SHE DID IT. From her earliest years,
    Mae planned to be a scientist. Her parents. . .
    http://www.nst.gov/od/lpa/nstw/kids/cards/world/mae.htm

Use the screen to answer the questions.

1 What is the name of the search engine used?

Fast Finder

2 What is the subject of the search?

Mae Jemison

3 How many web sites were found?

2

4 How could you change your search to find information about other women astronauts?

I don't know

TEST POWER

DIRECTIONS:

Read the story. Then read each question about the story.

SAMPLE

Going to the Store

"Paul, do you want to go with me?" Paul's father asked him.

"Sure, Dad. Are we going to the food store?" asked Paul.

"Yes," said his father.

"I'll get my coat," said Paul. Paul and his father didn't have anything to make for dinner. They needed to go to the store to buy some groceries.

Food shopping was always a lot of fun for Paul and his dad.

1 What will Paul and his father do when they get home?
   - ● Make dinner.
   - ○ Go out to eat at a restaurant.
   - ○ Go right to sleep.

2 What does the word groceries mean?
   - ● Food
   - ○ Dishes
   - ○ Socks

Look for clues around the underlined word to help you figure out what it means.

The Merry-Go-Round

The merry-go-round
    whirls round and round
    in giant circles on the ground.

And the horses run
    an exciting race
    while the wind blows music in your face.

Then the whole world spins
    to a colored tune
    but the ride is over much too soon.

—by Myra Cohn Livingston

125

Just Between Us

Doves

Although I saw you
The day before yesterday,
And yesterday and today,
This much is true—
I want to see you tomorrow, too!

by Masahito

My Friends

Here comes my friend Sue,
She went to the zoo.
A big baboon
Stole her spoon,
So he could eat his stew!

Here comes my friend Lew,
He tried something new.
He put on his coat
And sat in a boat
And fished in the sea so blue!

Meet the Author

When Stuart J. Murphy was in school, he didn't think math was fun. Now that he is grown up, Mr. Murphy is helping to change the way kids feel about math. He writes books that make math a lot of fun. Mr. Murphy gets ideas for his books by visiting children in schools and libraries all over the United States. He says, "I also get ideas from events that happened when my children were young, and from things that have happened in my life."

Meet the Illustrator

Tricia Tusa is the author and illustrator of several children's books. She gets her ideas by watching the people around her. "I study people's faces down the aisles at the grocery store and the laundromat. I listen in on people talking at the hardware store." Her pet rabbit, Mrs. Stewart, also gives Ms. Tusa story ideas. "Mrs. Stewart thumps around the house, but will sometimes stop to chat," she says.

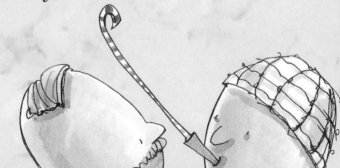

Lemonade for Sale

By Stuart J. Murphy

Illustrated by Tricia Tusa

The members of the Elm Street Kids' Club
were feeling glum.

"Our clubhouse is falling down, and our piggybank is empty," Meg said.

"I know how we can make some money,"
said Matthew. "Let's sell lemonade."

Danny said, "I bet if we can sell about 30
or 40 cups each day for a week, we'll make
enough money to fix our clubhouse. Let's keep
track of our sales."

Sheri said, "I can make a bar graph. I'll list
the number of cups up the side like this. I'll
show the days of the week along the bottom
like this."

On Monday they set up their corner stand.

When people walked by, Petey, Meg's pet parrot, squawked, "Lemonade for sale! Lemonade for sale!"

Matthew squeezed the lemons.

Meg mixed in some sugar.

Danny shook it up with ice and poured
it into cups.

Sheri kept track of how many
cups they sold.

Sheri announced, "We sold 30 cups today. I'll fill in the bar above Monday up to the 30 on the side."

"Not bad," said Danny.

"Not bad. Not bad," chattered Petey.

On Tuesday Petey squawked again, "Lemonade for sale! Lemonade for sale!" and more people came by.

Matthew squeezed more lemons.

Meg mixed in more sugar.

Danny shook it up with ice and poured it into more cups.

Sheri kept track of how many cups they sold.

Sheri shouted, "We sold 40 cups today. I'll
fill in the bar above Tuesday up to the number
40. The bars show that our sales are going up."

"Things are looking good," said Meg.

"Looking good. Looking good," chattered Petey.

141

On Wednesday Petey squawked, "Lemonade for sale!" so many times that most of the neighborhood stopped by.

Matthew squeezed
even more lemons.

Meg mixed in even
more sugar.

Danny shook it up with ice and poured
it into even more cups.

Sheri kept track of how
many cups they sold.

Sheri yelled, "We sold 56 cups today. I'll fill in Wednesday's bar up to a little more than halfway between 50 and 60."

"That's great," shouted Matthew.

"That's great! That's great!" bragged Petey.

They opened again on Thursday, but something was wrong. No matter how many times Petey squawked, "Lemonade for sale!" hardly anyone stopped by.

Matthew squeezed just a few lemons.

Meg mixed in only a couple of spoonfuls of sugar.

Danny's ice melted while he waited.

Sheri kept track of the few cups that they sold.

Sheri said, "We sold only 24 cups today. Thursday's bar is way down low."

"There goes our clubhouse," said Danny sadly.

Petey didn't make a sound.

"I think I know what's going on," said Matthew. "Look!" He pointed down the street. "There's someone juggling on that corner, and everyone's going over there to watch."

"Let's check it out," said Meg.

Danny asked the juggler, "Who are you?"

"I'm Jed," said the juggler. "I just moved here."

Sheri had an idea.

She whispered something to Jed.

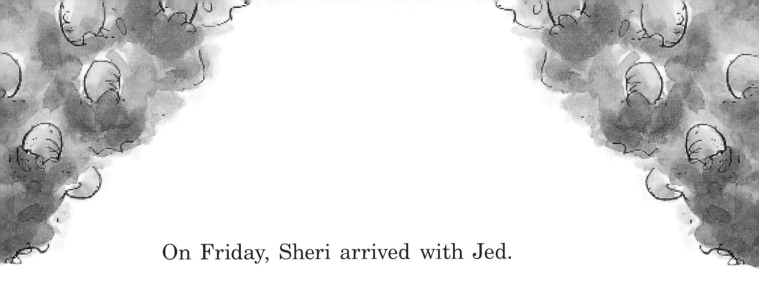

On Friday, Sheri arrived with Jed.

"Jed's going to juggle right next to our stand," Sheri said.

That day Petey squawked, Jed juggled, and more people came by than ever before.

Matthew squeezed loads of lemons.

Meg mixed in tons of sugar.

Danny shook it up with lots of ice and almost ran out of cups.

Sheri could hardly keep track of
how many cups they sold.

"We sold so many cups today that our sales
are over the top. We have enough money to
rebuild our clubhouse."

"Hooray!" they all shouted. "Jed! Jed! Will
you join our club?"

"You bet!" said Jed.

"You bet! You bet!" squawked Petey.

Story Questions & Activities

1 Why does the Elm Street Kids' Club want to raise money?

2 Sheri brought Jed the Juggler to the lemonade stand. How did this solve the problem the club had?

3 Why did the club members want to keep track of the money they made?

4 What is this story mostly about?

5 José and his family work together on Rio Ranch. How do the characters in "Lemonade for Sale" work together?

Write a Letter

Suppose that you were going to have a school fair. What kinds of fun things would be at your fair? Write a letter to your family describing your fair. Use describing words as you tell them what kinds of games, food or crafts will be there.

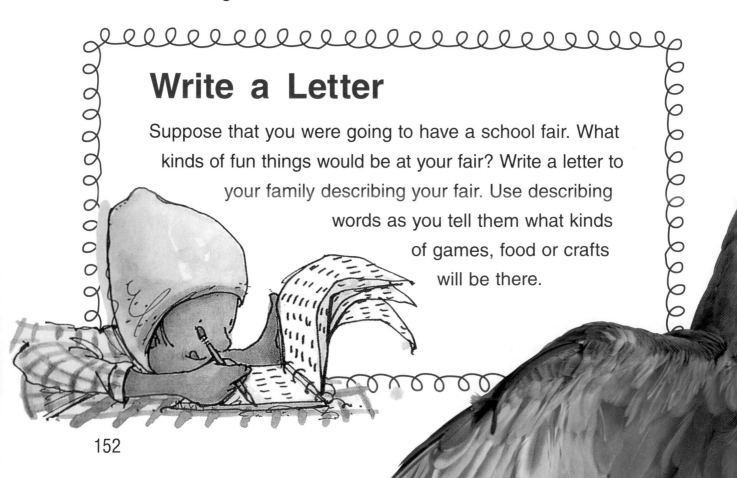

Make Lemonade

Make lemonade with your class. Pour 1 cup of lemon juice, 1 cup of sugar, and 6 cups of water into a pitcher. Stir and add ice cubes. If you wanted to make two pitchers of lemonade, how much of each ingredient would you need?

A Lemonade Stand

Petey the Parrot tells people about the lemonade stand in "Lemonade for Sale." Suppose you had a lemonade stand. Make a poster that tells about your lemonade sale. Be sure to include prices.

Find Out More

The characters in "Lemonade for Sale" use a recipe to make lemonade. Find a recipe for a food you like. Draw a picture of this food and paste it to your recipe. Share your recipe with the class.

Read a Graph

Dan's Fruit Stand Sales

apples

pears

bananas

Use the graph to answer the questions.

1 What does the graph show? *Dan's Fruit Stand Sales*

2 How many pears were sold at Dan's fruit stand? *8*

3 Which fruit did Dan sell the most of? *apples*

4 How many more apples than bananas were sold? *7*

TEST POWER

DIRECTIONS:

Read the story. Then read each question about the story.

SAMPLE

The Library

Our town has a library. It has many books. My friend Frank goes there. He likes books a lot. He takes three or four books home to read. They have stories about far-away places and people.

He pretends to be the characters in the books. Some days, he is a farmer. Some days, he is a doctor. Some days, he is a teacher. Yesterday, Frank was a painter. He painted big, colorful bugs on his paper.

Frank takes his books back to the library when he is done. Then he gets new ones. It's a good thing that the library has so many books.

1   In this story, what does Frank pretend to be?
   ○ The characters in his books
   ○ A giant who lives in the clouds
   ○ A librarian

2   How does Frank feel about the library?
   ○ He likes it.
   ○ He doesn't like it.
   ○ It scares him.

The Lost and Found Kite

Roy went out to fly his kite,
He ran around the hill.
The kite flew up above his house,
And then flew higher still.
The kite string broke, Roy gave a shout,
But the wind took it away.
The kite flew on, up past the clouds.
Down to the ground it fell.
Who found Roy's kite?
Roy's friend Joy—
She brought it back next day!

Meet
EZRA JACK KEATS

Ezra Jack Keats made the pictures in *A Letter to Amy* by painting over pieces of paper that he cut, tore, and pasted down.

Mr. Keats got the idea for Peter from some pictures of a child that he cut out of a newspaper. He had these pictures for 22 years before he made the first book with  Peter in it. Other books by Ezra Jack Keats about Peter include *The Snowy Day, Whistle for Willie,* and *Peter's Chair.*

158

EZRA JACK KEATS

It is this Saturday at 2.

A
LETTER
TO AMY

"I'm writing a letter to Amy.

I'm inviting her to my party," Peter announced.

"Why don't you just ask her? You didn't write
to anyone else," said his mother.

Peter stared at the sheet of paper for a while and said,
"We-e-el-l, this way it's sort of special."

He folded the letter quite a few times,
put it in the envelope, and sealed it.
"Now I'll mail it," he said.
"What did you write?" his mother asked.
WILL YOU PLEASE COME
TO MY BIRTHDAY PARTY. PETER.
"You should tell her when to come."
So he wrote on the back of the envelope:
IT IS THIS SATURDAY AT 2.
"Now I'll mail it."
"Put on a stamp."
He did, and started to leave.
"Wear your raincoat. It looks like rain."
He put it on and said, "It looks like rain.
You'd better stay in, Willie,"
and ran out to mail his letter.

Walking to the mailbox, Peter looked at the sky.
Dark clouds raced across it like wild horses.
He glanced up at Amy's window. She wasn't there.
Only Pepe, her parrot, sat peering down.
"Willie! Didn't I tell you to stay home?"

Peter thought, What will the boys say
when they see a girl at my party?
Suddenly there was a flash of lightning
and a roar of thunder!
A strong wind blew the letter out of his hand!

Peter chased the letter.
He tried to stop it with his foot, but it blew away.

Then it flew high into the air—

and landed, skipping across a hopscotch game.

The letter blew this way and that.
Peter chased it this way and that.
He couldn't catch it.

Big drops of rain began to fall.
Just then someone turned the corner.
It was Amy! She waved to him.
The letter flew right toward her.

She mustn't see it, or the surprise will be spoiled!
They both ran for the letter.

In his great hurry, Peter bumped into Amy.
He caught the letter before she could see it was for her.

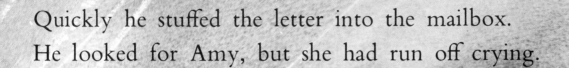
Quickly he stuffed the letter into the mailbox.
He looked for Amy, but she had run off crying.

Now she'll never come to my party, thought Peter.
He saw his reflection in the street.
It looked all mixed up.

When Peter got back to his house, his mother asked, "Did you mail your letter?"

"Yes," he said sadly.

Saturday came at last.
Everybody arrived but Amy.

"Shall I bring the cake out now?" his mother asked Peter.

"Let's wait a little," said Peter.

"Now! Bring it out now!" chanted the boys.

"All right," said Peter slowly, "bring it out now."

Just then the door opened.
In walked Amy with her parrot!
"A girl—ugh!" said Eddie.

"Yay it's cool" screamed peter

"Happy Birthday, Peter!" said Amy.
"HAAPPY BIRRRTHDAY, PEEETERRR!"
repeated the parrot.

Peter's mother brought in the cake she had baked
and lit the candles. Everyone sang.
"Make a wish!" cried Amy.
"Wish for a truck full of ice cream!" shouted Eddie.
"A store full of candy and no stomach-ache!"

But Peter made his own wish,
and blew out all the candles at once.

Story Questions & Activities

1 What happens to the letter when Peter tries to put it in the mailbox?

2 Why does Peter worry about inviting a girl to his party?

3 What do you think Peter wishes for? Tell why you think so.

4 What is this story mostly about?

5 If Peter met Luka from "Luka's Quilt," what kind of advice could they give each other to help solve their problems?

Write a Journal Entry

What if you wished to go on a trip for your birthday and you got your wish? Where would you like to go? Write a journal entry describing your trip. What is the place like? How does it make you feel? Use all of your senses to create the look, smell, and sounds of the place.

Write an Address

There are usually four lines to an address: the name, house or apartment number and street, city and state, and the ZIP code. Write a short note to a friend or relative. Put it in an envelope. Then address the envelope, put a stamp on it, and send it or give it to the person.

Create a Card

Create a birthday card for someone you know. Draw or cut out a picture for the front of the card. Then, write a poem or other greeting for the inside that tells your feelings.

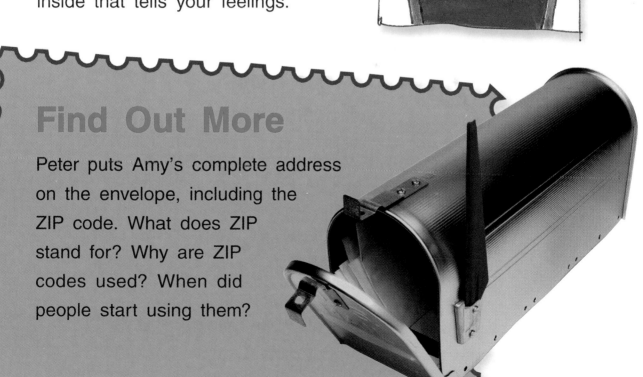

Find Out More

Peter puts Amy's complete address on the envelope, including the ZIP code. What does ZIP stand for? Why are ZIP codes used? When did people start using them?

Use a Diagram

Letter carriers pick up letters from mailboxes. They bring the letters to the Post Office. At the Post Office, workers sort the mail. Then the mail is put into trucks and delivered on mail routes.

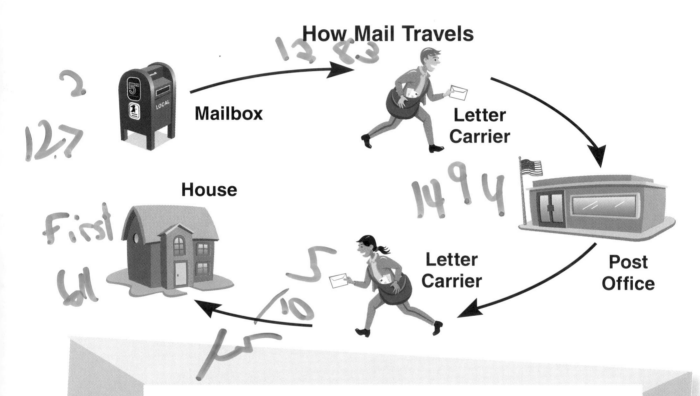

How Mail Travels

Mailbox

Letter Carrier

Post Office

Letter Carrier

House

Use the diagram to answer the questions.

1 Where does the route of the letter start?

2 Where does the route of the letter end?

3 Where does the mail carrier pick up letters?

4 Tell, in order, the places a letter goes as it travels along a mail route.

190

TEST POWER

Check your understanding of the story as you read it.

DIRECTIONS:
Read the story. Then read each question about the story.

SAMPLE

Willie in the Apple Orchard

Willie took a walk around the apple trees. "I'll pick some apples so I can make a pie," thought Willie.

He climbed into a tree. He climbed higher and higher. Some branches bent when he stepped on them. He stopped and picked some apples. Then, he started to climb down.

SNAP! One of Willie's feet broke a branch. He slid down the tree. But he was able to grab the tree trunk. Willie put his other foot onto a big branch.

"Wow," said Willie, "that was close. I better be more careful next time." He climbed down the tree. Then, he picked up his apples and went home to make his apple pie.

1 When Willie started to fall, he—
   ● grabbed onto the tree's trunk
   ○ jumped out of the tree
   ○ began to cry

2 How does Willie feel when he starts to slide down the tree?
   ● Scared
   ○ Sleepy
   ○ Lazy

A Surprise for Tim

Tim glared.
Toby and Clare
Had gone to the store
And left him there.
"I don't care,"
said Tim with a glare.
"Who wants to go the store anymore?"
Then Toby and Clare suddenly appeared
With a big red box and a shiny gold pear.
"Happy Birthday, Tim!" they cheered.
"You're our favorite hare!"

MEET
ELIZABETH WINTHROP

Elizabeth Winthrop wrote *The Best Friends Club* because of what happened to her as a child. She says, "I grew up with five brothers. Like Lizzie, I always made rules, but they paid no attention to me."

Ms. Winthrop thinks friendship is important to all children. She adds, "My children were always worried about having friends. How do I get a best friend? Will I keep her or him? What's a best friend like?"

She says about her writing, "When I write, I go into myself and find out what I'm feeling."

She adds, "I love writing for children. *The Best Friends Club* is a sequel to *Lizzie and Harold*. I knew their story wasn't over, so I wrote another one."

MEET MARTHA WESTON

Martha Weston was very excited about illustrating *The Best Friends Club* because she likes Lizzie so much.

She explains, "As a child, I was really bossy and had to show everyone how to do everything. Everything had to be done the way I wanted it to be done. Lizzie is like that, and I love her because she reminds me of myself.

"When I began drawing Lizzie and Harold, I asked my daughter and her friend to model for me. I asked them to do the things that Lizzie and Harold do in the story, and I took pictures of them. I paid them ten cents each for every picture I took."

Lizzie and Harold

by Elizabeth Winthrop
pictures by Martha Weston

THE BEST FRIENDS CLUB

CLUB

BY ELIZABETH WINTHROP
ILLUSTRATED BY MARTHA WESTON

Lizzie and Harold were best friends.
Harold taught Lizzie how to do cat's cradle.
Lizzie taught Harold how to play running bases.

Lizzie shared her trick-or-treat candy with Harold, and Harold let Lizzie ride his big red bike.

They always walked home from school together.

"Let's start a best friends club," Lizzie said one day.

"Great," said Harold. "We can meet under your porch. That will be our clubhouse."

Harold painted the sign.

It said

THE BF CLUB.

"Now write *Members Only*," said Lizzie.

"You write it," said Harold. "My teacher says my M's are too fat."

So Lizzie wrote *Members Only*.

"Who are the members?" Harold asked.

"You and me," said Lizzie.
"That's all?"
"Yes," said Lizzie. "You can be the president and I'll be the vice-president. The president gets to write down all the rules."

"You be the president," Harold said. "Your writing is better than mine."

"All right, then I'll be president," said Lizzie. "Now we'll make up the rules."

"Rule number one," said Harold. "The club meets under Lizzie's porch."

"Right," said Lizzie. "Rule number two. Nobody else can be in the club."

"Rule number three," said Harold. He thought for a long time. "I can't think of any more."

"Rule number three," said Lizzie. "Lizzie and Harold walk home from school together every day."

"Rule number four," said Harold. "Everybody in the club knows cat's cradle."

They heard voices. Someone was walking by. They could see two pairs of feet.

"It's Christina," whispered Lizzie. "She always wears those black party shoes."

"And Douglas," Harold whispered back. "His shoelaces are always untied."

"I'm only having Nancy and Amy and Stacey to my birthday party," they heard Christina say.

"My mother said I could have my whole class," Douglas answered. "We're going to play baseball."

"Oh goody," said Harold. "That means I'll be invited to Douglas's birthday party."

"I won't," Lizzie said gloomily. She was in a different class.

The next day, Harold came out of his classroom with Douglas.

"He wants to walk home with us," Harold said to Lizzie.

"He can't," said Lizzie.

"Why not?" asked Harold.

"Harold, remember the rules. We're best friends and we always walk home together," Lizzie said. "Just you and me."

"Oh yeah," said Harold. "I forgot."

Douglas looked very sad.

"Sorry, Douglas," Harold said. "See you tomorrow."

"Douglas's ears stick out," Lizzie said on the way home.

"So what?" said Harold.

"His shoelaces are always dripping," said Lizzie.

"I don't care about that," said Harold.

"I'll meet you in the clubhouse after snacks," said Lizzie.

"I can't come today," said Harold. "My mother wants me home."

200

Lizzie sat in the clubhouse all by herself.

She wrote down more rules.

They said

5. Best friends don't go to other people's birthday parties.

6. People with funny ears and drippy shoelaces are not allowed in the club.

The next day, Harold came out of his classroom with Douglas again.

"Douglas asked me to play at his house," said Harold.

"*Harold,*" said Lizzie. "What about the club?"

"What club?" asked Douglas.

"None of your business," said Lizzie.

"I'll come tomorrow," said Harold. "I promise."

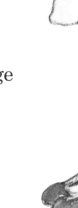

Lizzie watched them walk away together. She stuck out her tongue at them but Harold didn't turn around.

She went straight to the clubhouse and wrote down another rule. It said

7. Best friends don't go to other people's houses to play.

Then she threw a ball at the garage wall until suppertime.

"Douglas wants to be in the club," said Harold the next day.

"He can't be," said Lizzie. "Only best friends are allowed in this club."

She showed him all the new rules she had written down.

"This club is no fun," said Harold. "It has too many rules. I quit."

He crawled out from under the porch and walked home.

Lizzie took down his sign and put up a new one.

Douglas came down the street.

He was riding Harold's new bicycle.

Harold was chasing after him.

When Harold saw the sign, he stopped and read it.

"What does it say?" asked Douglas.

"It says, 'Lizzie's Club. Nobody Else Allowed,'"
Harold said.

Harold leaned over and looked at Lizzie. "You can't
have a club with only one person," he said.

"*I* can," said Lizzie.

"A three-person club is more fun," said Harold.
"Douglas knows how to do cat's cradle."

"But he's not a best friend,"
said Lizzie.

"It'll be a different kind of club," said Harold.
"We'll make up a new name."
"Maybe," said Lizzie.
She sat under the porch and watched them.
First they played bicycle tag.
Then they threw the ball at her garage wall.

"Want to play running bases?" Lizzie asked.

"I don't know how," said Douglas.

"I'll teach you," said Lizzie.

They took turns being the runner. Lizzie was the fastest.

Douglas whispered something to Harold.

"Douglas wants you to come to his birthday party," said Harold.

Then Lizzie whispered something to Harold.

"Lizzie says yes," Harold said to Douglas.

"And I've thought of a new name for the club," said Lizzie. "Douglas can be in it too."

"Oh boy!" said Douglas.

"You can be the first member. I am the president and Harold is the vice-president," said Lizzie.

"That's okay with me," said Harold.

"Me too," said Douglas.

It was getting dark.

Douglas went home for supper.

Lizzie crawled back under the porch. She tore up her sign and her list of rules.

"What's the new name for the club?" Harold asked.

"I'll show you," said Lizzie.

She sat down and wrote in great big letters
THE NO RULES CLUB.

Harold smiled.

He stuck up the sign with a thumbtack.

Then they both went upstairs to Lizzie's house
for supper.

Story Questions & Activities

1 Who makes all of the rules for the Best Friends Club?

2 Why doesn't Lizzie want Douglas to be in the club? Tell how you know.

3 Why do you think Lizzie lets Douglas in the club at the end of the story? Tell why you think so.

4 What is this story mostly about?

5 How might the misunderstandings in "The Best Friends Club" and "A Letter to Amy" have been avoided?

Write an Article

Suppose you created your dream clubhouse and the local paper asked you to write an article describing it. Where is it? What materials were used? What did you put inside? How many details can you think of to describe your dream clubhouse?

Teach Your Favorite Game

Write directions for one of your favorite games. It could be a ball game, a card game, checkers, or chess. You could even make up your own game. Add pictures to help make your directions clearer. Share the directions with friends and teach them how to play.

Draw Your Dream Clubhouse

Imagine that you could have any clubhouse in the world. What would it look like? What would you put in it? Draw a picture showing your clubhouse and what you would put inside it.

Find Out More

Find out the name of one club in your community. What kinds of things do its members like to do?

Make a Cat's Cradle

Tie the two ends of a string together. Loop the string around each hand. Next, loop the string around your four fingers. Slip your middle finger under the string that crosses your other palm and pull. Do this with both middle fingers. You have made a cat's cradle.

A. string

B. 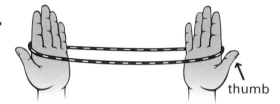 thumb

C.

D. middle finger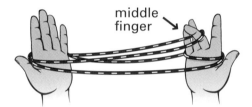

Use the diagram to answer the questions.

1 What materials do you need to make a cat's cradle?

A tied string

2 Look at picture B in the diagram. What finger is outside the string?

3 Look at picture C. Which fingers have a loop of the string around them?

4 Make a cat's cradle. Look at the pattern of the string. What shapes do you see?

214

TEST POWER

What does the story tell you about feelings?

DIRECTIONS:
Read the story. Then read each question about the story.

SAMPLE

Baxter Tries to Fly

Baxter was a curious bear. He wanted to live in a tree and to fly like a bird. One day Baxter went to see Ray Raven. "Can I live in your nest?" asked Baxter.

"Sure," said Ray. Baxter started to climb the tree, but he was too heavy. The branches broke when he stepped on them. "Can you show me how to fly?" he asked Ray. Ray flapped his wings and flew. Baxter flapped his arms, but he couldn't fly. Baxter frowned.

"Cheer up," said Ray. "Bears get to eat honey."

Baxter ate some honey and smiled. "You're right," Baxter said. "It's not so bad to be a bear."

1 How did Baxter feel after he tried to fly?
○ Tired
◉ Unhappy
○ Confused

2 Why is Baxter happy at the end of the story?
◉ He realizes that being a bear isn't so bad.
○ He finally learned how to fly.
○ He moved into Ray's nest.

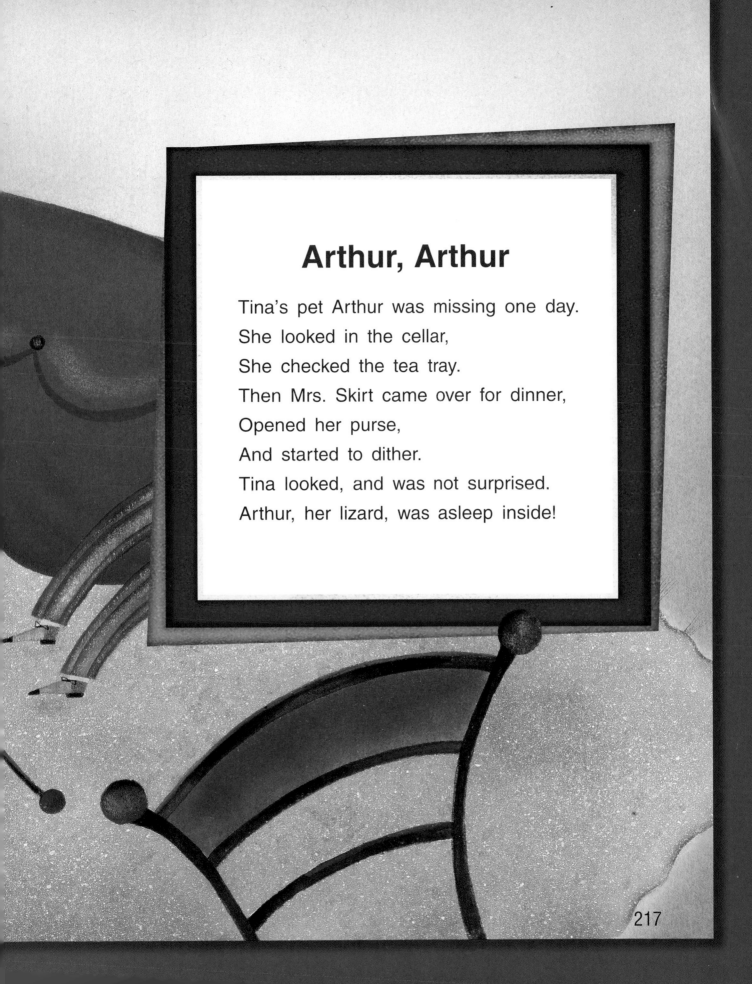

Arthur, Arthur

Tina's pet Arthur was missing one day.
She looked in the cellar,
She checked the tea tray.
Then Mrs. Skirt came over for dinner,
Opened her purse,
And started to dither.
Tina looked, and was not surprised.
Arthur, her lizard, was asleep inside!

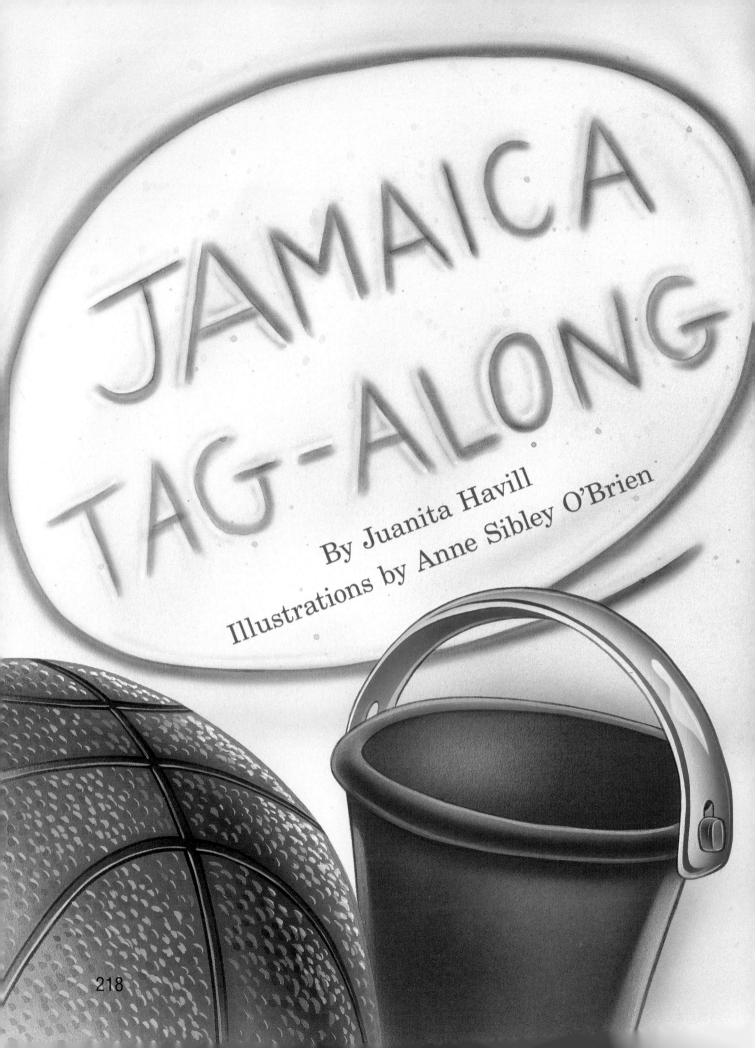

JAMAICA TAG-ALONG

By Juanita Havill

Illustrations by Anne Sibley O'Brien

Jamaica ran to the kitchen to answer the phone.
But her brother got there first.

"It's for me," Ossie said.

Jamaica stayed and listened to him talk.

"Sure," Ossie said. "I'll meet you at the court."

Ossie got his basketball from the closet. "I'm going to shoot baskets with Buzz."

"Can I come, too?" Jamaica said. "I don't have anything to do."

"Ah, Jamaica, call up your own friends."

"Everybody is busy today."

"I don't want you tagging along."

"I don't want to tag along," Jamaica said. "I just want to play basketball with you and Buzz."

"You're not old enough. We want to play serious ball."

Ossie dribbled his basketball down the sidewalk. Jamaica followed at a distance on her bike.

Buzz was already at the school court, shooting baskets with Jed and Maurice.

She parked her bike by the bushes and crept to the corner of the school building to watch.

That's not fair, Jamaica thought. Maurice is shorter than I am.

Pom, pa-pom, pa-pom, pom, pom.

The boys started playing, Ossie and Jed against Buzz and Maurice.

Jamaica sneaked to the edge of the court.

Maurice missed a shot and the ball came bouncing toward her. Jamaica jumped. "I've got the ball," she yelled.

"Jamaica!" Ossie was so surprised he tripped over
Buzz. They both fell down.

Jamaica dribbled to the basket and tossed the ball.
It whirled around the rim and flew out.

"I almost made it," Jamaica shouted. "Can I be on your team, Ossie?"

"No. N-O, Jamaica. I told you not to tag along."

"It's not fair. You let Maurice play."

"We need two on a team. Why don't you go play on the swings and stay out of the way?"

"I still think it's not fair." Jamaica walked slowly over to the sandlot.

She started to swing, but a little boy kept walking in front of her. His mom should keep him out of the way, Jamaica thought.

She looked up and saw a woman pushing a baby
back and forth in a stroller.

Jamaica sat down in the sand and began to
dig. She made a big pile with the wet sand from
underneath. She scooped sand from the mound to
form a wall.

"Berto help," said the little boy. He sprinkled
dry sand on the walls.

"Don't," said Jamaica. "You'll just mess it up."
Jamaica turned her back.

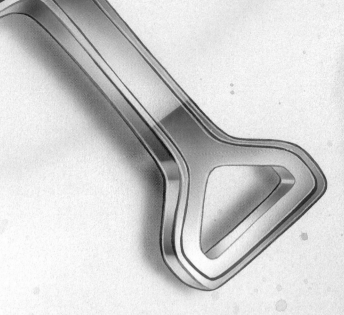

She piled the wet sand high. She made a castle with towers. She dug a ditch around the wall.

Jamaica turned to see if Berto was still there. He stood watching. Then he tried to step over the ditch, and his foot smashed the wall.

"Stay away from my castle," Jamaica said.

"Berto," the woman pushing the stroller said, "leave this girl alone. Big kids don't like to be bothered by little kids."

"That's what my brother always says," Jamaica said. She started to repair the castle. Then she thought, but I don't like my brother to say that. It hurts my feelings.

Jamaica smoothed the wall. "See, Berto, like that. You can help me make a bigger castle if you're very careful."

Jamaica and Berto made a giant castle. They put water from the drinking fountain in the moat.

"Wow," Ossie said when the game was over and
the other boys went home. "Need some help?"
"If you want to," Jamaica said.

Jamaica, Berto, and Ossie worked together on the castle.

Jamaica didn't even mind if Ossie tagged along.

MEET JUANITA HAVILL

Juanita Havill has been telling stories for a long time. As a young child, Ms. Havill made up stories. Her stories were important to her. They let her make believe she could do all kinds of fun things. When she grew up, she became a teacher and visited many places. But she kept on writing. She took a writing class. She found that she liked to write for children. By now, she has written many children's books. Ms. Havill says, "I write to find out what I think, to give form to thought."

MEET ANNE SIBLEY O'BRIEN

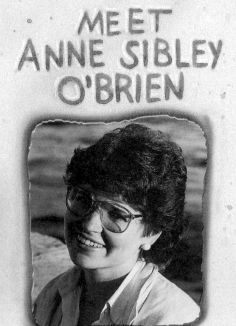

Anne Sibley O'Brien was born in Chicago, Illinois. Most of her childhood was spent in Korea. She never forgot what it was like to live in another country. She learned about many other ways of life. Today Ms. O'Brien's art shows peoples of all colors. She has also drawn pictures for another book about Jamaica. In both books she worked hard to make the people seem real. She hoped to show how the members of Jamaica's family love each other.

1 Where does Jamaica follow her brother?

2 Why does Jamaica decide to let Berto help her with the castle?

3 How do you think Jamaica's brother feels when Jamaica invites him to help build the sand castle?

4 What is this story about?

5 Jamaica and Lizzie from "The Best Friends Club" have both felt left out. What is the same about their experiences? What is different?

Write a Character Description

Imagine a character similar to Jamaica trying to convince an older brother or sister to let her or him join in an activity. What is this person's name? What does this character want to do? How does your character look and feel at this moment?

Counting Favorites

Maybe Jamaica wouldn't have followed Ossie if she had something she liked to do by herself. Make a list of things people like to do by themselves. Ask your classmates to choose their favorites. Keep track of their answers.

Act It Out

With a partner, write a short scene in which an older child does not want a younger child to tag along. Act it out.

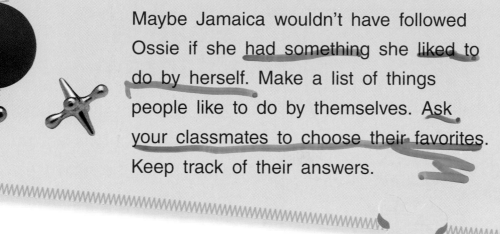

Find Out More

Jamaica builds a sand castle. Find out more about castles. What were they built out of? What are different parts of castles? Find a picture of a famous castle.

241

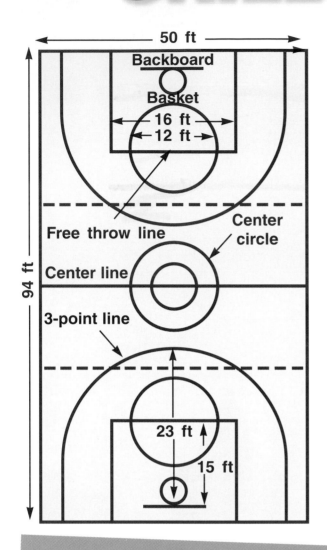

50 ft

Backboard

Basket

16 ft

12 ft

94 ft

Free throw line

Center circle

Center line

3-point line

23 ft

15 ft

Read a Diagram

This diagram shows how a basketball court is set up. It also shows the side view of the basket.

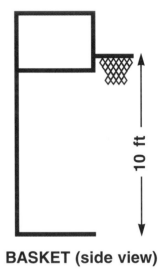

10 ft

BASKET (side view)

Use the diagram to answer the questions.

1 How high is the basket from the floor?

2 How wide is the court?

3 How far is the backboard from the 3-point line?

4 If a player ran from one backboard to the other, about how far would the player run?

TEST POWER

How does the character solve the problem?

DIRECTIONS:
Read the story. Then read each question about the story.

SAMPLE

At the Zoo

Juanita was very happy. Today she was going to the zoo. Juanita had been there before. She remembered how funny the monkeys were.

Juanita wanted to see the birds. She also wanted to see the monkeys again. After she saw the birds, she looked for the monkeys. Juanita looked up one path and down another. She still could not find the monkeys. Then, Juanita remembered that she had a map for the zoo. She looked at her map and found her way to the monkeys.

When she walked up close to the cage, a monkey came closer. He made funny faces at her. Juanita made a face back. The monkey laughed, and so did Juanita. Juanita liked the monkeys most of all.

1 How does Juanita finally find the monkeys?
- ○ She asks for some help.
- ● She looks at her map.
- ○ She hears them howling.

2 Why does Juanita like the monkeys best?
- ○ They are small.
- ○ They sit quietly.
- ● They make her laugh.

243

244

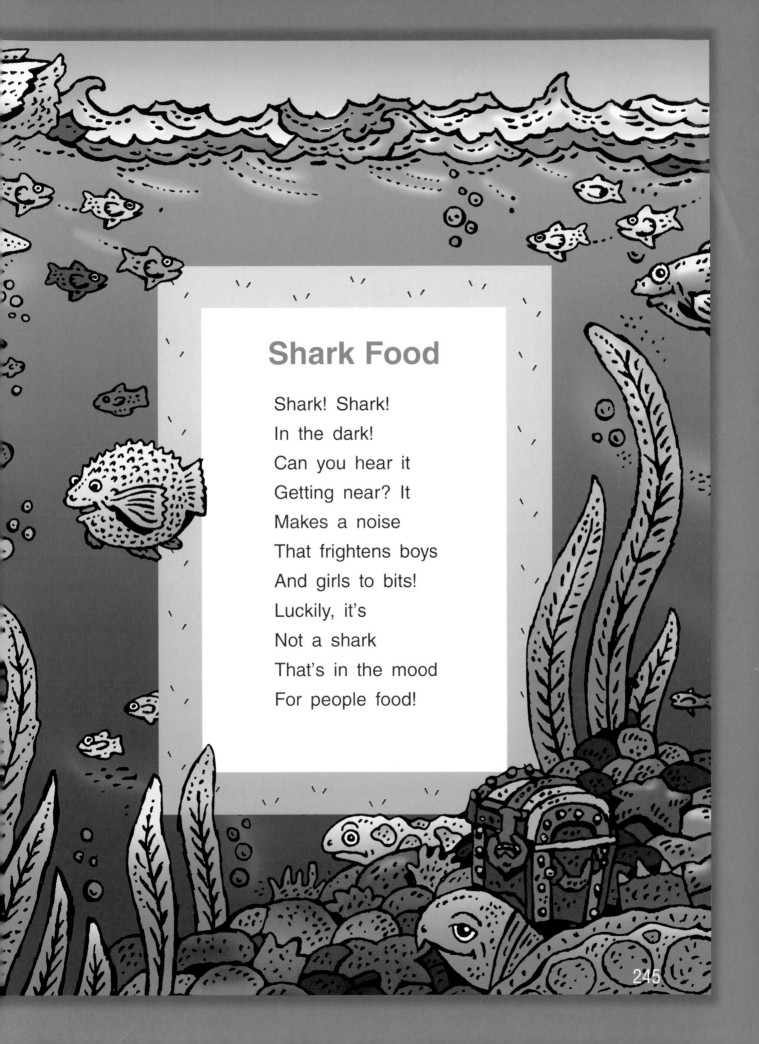

Shark Food

Shark! Shark!
In the dark!
Can you hear it
Getting near? It
Makes a noise
That frightens boys
And girls to bits!
Luckily, it's
Not a shark
That's in the mood
For people food!

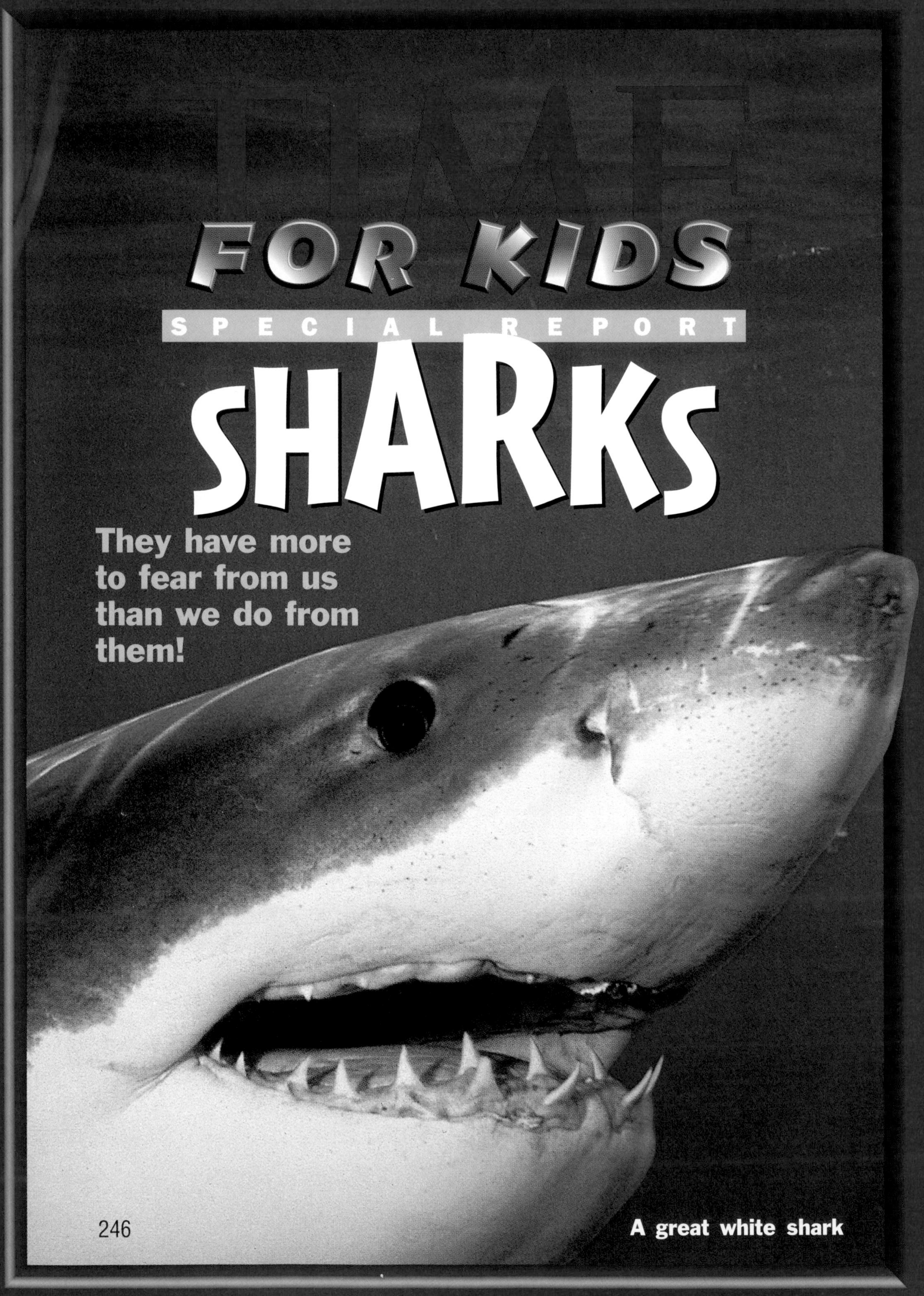
TIME
FOR KIDS
SPECIAL REPORT
SHARKS
They have more to fear from us than we do from them!

A great white shark

Under Attack!

Sharks have swum the seas for millions of years. Now they are in danger of disappearing.

Carl Meyer is in a small boat near Hawaii. He is using a rope to fish. That may sound kind of funny. But he is fishing for a tiger shark. Meyer finds the shark and ropes it in. Meyer does not want to hurt the shark. He wants to look at it. Carl Meyer is a scientist. He wants to understand why sharks act the way they do. We have much to learn and little to fear from these fish.

People have always been afraid of sharks. But sharks are happier eating seals or fish than people. Scientists say that sharks may mistake people in the water for sea animals. A person's flapping feet may look like a fish to a hungry shark.

A hammerhead shark has its eyes on the side of its head.

247

Gray reef sharks swim in the Pacific Ocean.

People kill 100 million sharks every year. Many people love to eat shark meat. Some people wear belts made of shark skin. Many sharks get caught in fishing nets.

What does this mean for sharks? Some kinds of sharks may die out in 10 years. That would be very bad. After all, these fish have been swimming around for 400 million years. That means sharks were around 100 million years before the dinosaurs.

Scientists can watch sharks from a diving cage. A great white shark tries to take a bite out of this one.

Sharks can help people in many ways. We can learn lessons from them.

A shark's body can fight off sickness better than a person's body. So sharks may teach us about fighting sicknesses in people.

Sharks keep other kinds of sea life at the right level by hunting them. If sharks were to die out, the food chain would be in trouble.

Many people are working to cut down on shark hunting. The U.S. and some other countries have put limits on shark catches. And scientists have put some kinds of sharks on a list of animals in danger.

As one shark scientist says, "Sharks are here for a reason, not to attack men, women, and children."

FIND OUT MORE
Visit our website:
www.mhschool.com/reading

*inter*NET
CONNECTION

DID YOU KNOW?
SUPER SHARK FACTS

- Sharks can swim for miles in a straight line.

- Sharks don't always chew their food. License plates, cups, and entire animals have been found inside them.

- The biggest shark is 50 feet long. The smallest is 5 inches long.

- When a shark loses a tooth, a new one moves up to take its place.

- Sharks have no bones. Their bodies are made of cartilage, like our noses.

Based on an article in *TIME FOR KIDS*.

Story Questions & Activities

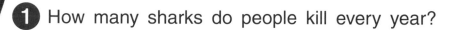

1 How many sharks do people kill every year?

2 What are some of the reasons that sharks are killed by people?

3 If sharks died out, why might the food chain be in trouble?

4 What is the main idea of this selection?

5 Antonio helps the calf in "Roundup at Rio Ranch." How can people help save sharks?

Write an Article

Can you name an animal other than a shark that is in danger? Write an article for a nature magazine describing this animal. What does it look like? What makes it special?

Make a Poster

Some kinds of sharks may die out in ten years. Make a poster telling why it is important to save the sharks and what people can do to help.

SOS!
Save Our Sharks

Don't buy
sharkskin belts

Compare the Oldest Animals

Sharks and dinosaurs are very different animals, but they were both on Earth millions of years ago. What else do sharks and dinosaurs have in common? Make a chart that shows facts about each.

Find Out More

The basking shark can be 50 feet long. The dwarf shark is five inches long. There are many different types of sharks. Find out the length of two other kinds of sharks.

251

Use a Bar Graph

Whales Seen
Montauk Whale Watch Association

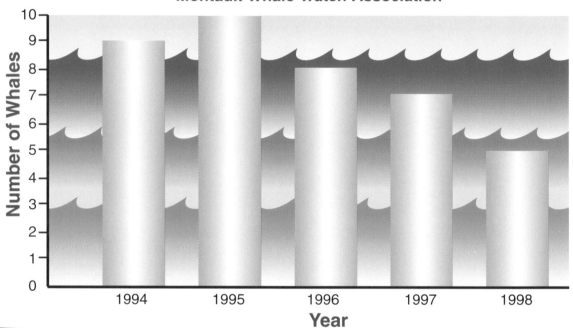

Use the graph to answer these questions.

1 How many whales were seen in 1997?

2 How many whales were seen in 1994?

3 In which year did the Montauk Whale Watch Association see the greatest number of whales?

4 What if 1999 were shown on the graph? Do you think the bar would be higher or lower than the bar for 1998? Why do you think so?

252

TEST POWER

How do you think the character feels at the beginning, middle, and end of the story?

DIRECTIONS:

Read the story. Then read each question about the story.

SAMPLE

Who Took Davey's Baseball Glove?

"Where did my baseball glove go?" Davey wondered. Tomorrow was the big game. He needed his glove to play. Davey looked under the bed. He looked in the closet. He couldn't find his glove anywhere.

Davey asked his dad for help. "Let me look in the garage," his dad said. But the glove wasn't there.

Davey's mom helped to look, too. She even looked in the kitchen. She couldn't find it either.

Just then, Davey's dog Fluffy came into the house. His nose was covered with dirt. Davey went outside and found his glove buried in the garden.

1 How does Davey feel when he can't find his glove?
○ Happy
◉ Worried
○ Silly

2 How does Davey know where to find his glove?
○ His father tells him where to look.
◉ His dog gives him a clue.
○ His mother says she saw it in the kitchen.

253

254

Four Generations

Sometimes when we go out for walks,
I listen while my father talks.

The thing he talks of most of all
Is how it was when he was small

And he went walking with *his* dad
And conversations that they had

About *his* father and the talks
They had when *they* went out for walks.

by Mary Ann Hoberman

255

Express Yourself

Cloud Dragons

What do you see
in the clouds so high?
What do you see in the sky?

Oh, I see dragons
that curl their tails
as they go slithering by.

What do you see
in the clouds so high?
What do you see? Tell me, do.

Oh, I see *caballitos*
that race the wind
high in the shimmering blue.

by Pat Mora

Chalk Drawings

Larry the Lamb brought out his chalk,
And drew a white sun on the sidewalk.
Betsy the Calf shook her head,
"Don't you know the sun should be red?"
Nate the Gnat buzzed up to see.
"Larry, I think it needs a tree."
Larry the Lamb thought for a while.
Then he gave his friends some chalk
And they all drew together on the sidewalk!

Meet Marc Brown

When Marc Brown was a boy, he spent most of his time drawing. His grandmother noticed his interest in art and encouraged him to make a career out of it.

Mr. Brown did not find a job as an artist right away. He worked as a cook and as a truck driver. But Mr. Brown was a better artist than truck driver. "I kept getting lost," he says.

His first book was *Arthur's Nose*, the first in a series of stories about a young aardvark with glasses. Since then, Arthur has become so popular that Mr. Brown has created a television series about him.

When he explains what it's like for him to work as both an author and illustrator, Mr. Brown says, "The artwork is easier for me than the writing."

Written and
Illustrated by MARC BROWN

ARTHUR
WRITES A STORY

On the chalkboard:

Write a story.
1. Have a beginning, a middle, and an end.
2. Use details.
3. Be creative.

Arthur's teacher, Mr. Ratburn, explained the homework.

"What should the story be about?" Arthur asked.

"Anything," Mr. Ratburn said. "Write about something that is important to you."

Arthur started his story the minute he
got home. He knew exactly what he wanted
to write about.

How I Got My Puppy Pal

I always wanted a dog, but first I had to prove I was responsible. So I started Arthur's Pet Business. My mom made me keep all the animals in the basement. It was a lot of work, but it was fun until I thought I lost Perky. But then I found her, and she had three puppies! And I got to keep one of them. That's how I got my dog Pal.

The End

Arthur read his story to D.W.

"That's a boring story," D.W. said. "Does it have to be real life? Because your life is so dull."

"I don't want to write a boring story," said Arthur.

"If it were me," D.W. suggested, "I'd make the story about getting an elephant."

265

The next day, Arthur read his new story to Buster.

"Did you like the part about the elephant puppies?" he asked.

"It's okay, I guess," said Buster. "I'm writing a cool story about outer space."

Maybe my story should take place on the moon, thought Arthur.

On Wednesday, Arthur read his newest story to the Brain.

"Scientifically speaking, elephants would weigh less on the moon, but wouldn't float that high," said the Brain.

"So you don't like it?" asked Arthur.

"A good story should be well researched," said the Brain. "Like mine: 'If I Had a Pet Stegosaurus in the Jurassic Period.'"

Arthur hurried to the library.

"What are all those books for?" asked Francine.

"Research," said Arthur. "I'm writing about my pet five-toed mammal of the genus *Loxodonta*."

"Your *what?*" asked Francine.

"My elephant!" Arthur explained.

"Oh," said Francine. "I'm putting jokes in my story."

All through dinner, Arthur worried about
his story.

"Please pass the corn," asked Father.

"Corn! That's it!" said Arthur. "Purple corn and blue elephants! On Planet Shmellafint! Now *that's* funny."

"Arthur is acting weirder than usual," said D.W.

On Thursday, everyone at the Sugar Bowl was talking about their stories.

"Last year, a kid wrote a country-western song for her story," said Prunella. "And she got an A+."

"How do you know?" asked Arthur.

"That kid was me," explained Prunella.
"Mr. Ratburn said I should send it to a record
company. It was *that* good."

"Wow!" said Arthur.

That night, Arthur's imagination went wild. He decided to turn his story into a song. He even made up a dance to go with it.

Later, he tried it out on his family.

"...Now this little boy

Can go home and enjoy

His own personal striped elephant.

And you will see

How happy he will be

Here on Planet ... Shmellafint!"

"Well," said Arthur. "What do you think?"

Mother and Father smiled.

"It's nice," said Grandma Thora. "But a little confusing."

"Too bad you can't dance," said D.W.

"What am I going to do?" said Arthur. "My story is due tomorrow."

That night Arthur didn't sleep very well.

The next day, Arthur worried until Mr. Ratburn finally called on him.

When Arthur's song and dance was over, the classroom was so quiet, it was almost spooky. Binky raised his hand. "Did that really happen?"

"Sort of," said Arthur. "It started as the story of how I got my dog."

"I'd like to hear that story," said Mr. Ratburn.

"The title was 'How I Got My Puppy Pal,'" said Arthur.

Arthur told how proud he was of his pet business and how scared he was when Perky disappeared. And he told how happy he was to find her under his bed and how surprised he was to see her three puppies.

"And the best part is," said Arthur, "I got to keep one!"

Buster said, "I like that story better than your other one."

"Great story!" said Binky.

"I think Arthur's story was the best!" said Francine.

"Good work," said Mr. Ratburn. "Of course, I expect you to write it all down by Monday."

Then Mr. Ratburn gave Arthur a gold sticker. "Oh, and one more thing," he said.

285

Story Questions & Activities

1 What does Arthur write his first story about?

2 Why does Arthur keep changing his story?

3 Why do you think Arthur's class likes the story about the puppy better than the one about the elephant?

4 What is this story mostly about?

5 How do both Arthur and Peter from "A Letter to Amy" show that they can think for themselves?

Write a Library Guide

Arthur had to go to the library to find books about elephants. Write a guide that tells how to find a book in your school library. Include any helpful hints you have learned from your librarians. Make sure all the steps are in the right order.

286

How I Got My Puppy Pal

Design a Story Cover

Reread Arthur's original story, "How I Got My Puppy Pal." Then draw or paint a cover for this story. Remember to put on the title and the name of the author.

Write a Poem

Write a poem about something that is important to you. Use colorful words that describe what you're writing about. Be creative.

Find Out More

Arthur is told that his story about elephants should be well researched. If you were writing a story about elephants, what important facts would you need to know?

STUDY SKILLS

Use a Dictionary

piano • plum

piano A large musical instrument with black and white keys. Jeff practices the *piano* every day.
   pi•an•o (pee AN oh) *noun, plural* **pianos**.

planet A large body that moves around the sun in a circle. There are nine *planets* that revolve around the sun.
   plan•et (PLAN it) *noun, plural* **planets.**

plum A fruit with smooth, purple skin. I like to have a *plum* with my lunch.
   plum (PLUM) *noun, plural* **plums.**

Use the part of a dictionary page to answer the questions.

1 Each word in a dictionary is called an **entry**. How many entries are on this part of a dictionary page?

2 What are the guide words on this page?

3 What is the meaning of the word *plum*?

4 How can a dictionary be helpful when you are reading or writing?

TEST POWER

Look for clues around the underlined word to figure out what it means.

DIRECTIONS:
Read the story. Then read each question about the story.

SAMPLE

The Island

Linda Lizard lived on an island. Her friends were Tom Turtle and Sandy Seagull.

Linda wanted to see if there were other islands. But she did not know how to swim. Tom offered to take Linda on his back so they could look. Sandy did not think it was safe. In fact, she thought it sounded <u>dangerous</u>.

Linda and Tom went into the water. The ocean was rough. Linda couldn't hold on. She began to slide into the sea. Sandy flew into the air from the beach. She picked Linda out of the water and took her back to shore. Linda was wet but not hurt.

"Thanks for saving me," Linda said to Sandy. Tom and Linda both said they would be more careful.

1 You know this story is make-believe because—

- ○ seagulls don't fly
- ● animals don't talk
- ○ there are no islands

2 In this passage, <u>dangerous</u> means—

- ○ that it is not fun
- ● that it is not safe
- ○ that it is not special

The Visit

A penguin went to visit my brother,
Then he asked to meet my mother.
He stayed with me and read my letters,
Ate my fish and wore my sweaters.
He only left when he discovered
That I had another brother.

✳ Meet James Stevenson

James Stevenson began writing and drawing as a child. He loved to watch movies and read comic books. He says that both activities influenced the books he writes for children.

He says, "I think that my experience and creative mind have been formed by movies and comic books. I like to write. I like to draw. I like to paint. And in writing picture books I found a way to tell a story without using just words."

When asked if he prefers drawing to writing, he said, "I think that drawing is the more childlike and natural. When you're a little kid, you grab crayons, you don't grab the typewriter. I think drawing is a little more fun than writing, but whether it's more satisfying by the time you're old, I don't know."

292

BEST WISHES, ED

by
JAMES STEVENSON

Ed lived on a big island of ice
with Betty, Freddy, Al,
and a lot of other penguins.
Every day they had fun
throwing snowballs
and sliding on the ice.

But they always watched out
for Ernest, the big whale.
Every time he went by . . .
SPLAT!
Ed and everybody got soaked.

"Watch what you are doing!"
Betty would yell.

But Ernest swam right by.
"Ernest doesn't even notice penguins,"
said Ed.

One night when Ed was asleep,
there was a loud cracking noise.
It sounded like ice breaking.
Ed thought it was a dream.

When Ed woke up in the morning,
he found that the island of ice
had broken in half.
He was all alone
on an island of his own.

Ed's friends got smaller
and smaller
as his island drifted away.
Ed watched until he couldn't
see them anymore.

Then he walked
around his island.
There was nobody on it at all.
At last he came to his
own footprints again.

Some birds flew over.
Ed waved,
but they did not wave back.
"I guess I will be here
the rest of my life," Ed said.
At the end of the day,
he wrote "I GIVE UP"
in big letters in the snow.
Then he went to sleep.

In the morning a tern woke him up.
"Hey," said the tern,
"did you write that thing in the snow?"

"Yes," said Ed.

"Could you write something
for me?" asked the tern.

"I guess so," said Ed.
"What do you want?"

"Tell my friends to meet me
at the blue iceberg," said the tern.
"And sign it 'Talbot.'
That is my name."

Talbot flew away,
and Ed wrote the message.

MEET
TALBOT
AT THE
BLUE
ICEBERG

Pretty soon, Talbot's friends
flew over and read the message.
They waved to Ed,
and Ed waved back.

HAROLD:
YOUR SUPPER IS READY

All day long, birds stopped and asked Ed
to write messages for them.
By the end of the day, the whole island
was covered with messages.
Ed was very tired.

DOROTHY:
MARTHA IS
LOOKING FOR YOU

GEORGE
MARY
IS AT

Talbot landed and gave Ed a fish.
"You are doing a great job,"
said Talbot.
"How come you look so gloomy?"

"I miss my friends
on my old island," said Ed.

"Where is your old island?"
asked Talbot.

"Way over there someplace,"
said Ed.

"Too bad you can't fly," said Talbot.
"You could spot it from the air."

"Well, I can't fly," said Ed.

"It's not very hard," said Talbot.

"It is for penguins," said Ed.

Talbot flew away.
"I guess I will spend the rest
of my life writing messages,"
Ed said to himself.

When Ed got up the next morning,
he found a surprise.

ED - THERE'S
A MESSAGE
FOR YOU !

FOLLOW THE ARROWS

SIT HERE AND WAIT → X

He followed the arrows
until he came to another message.

He sat down on the X
and waited.

Suddenly there was a great SPLAT!
Ed was soaked.
It was Ernest.
"I understand you are looking
for a ride to that island
with all the penguins on it,"
said Ernest.

"How did you know?" asked Ed.

"Talbot told me," said Ernest.
"Hop aboard."

"Wait one second," said Ed.
"I have to leave a message."

"Well, make it snappy," said Ernest.
"I have other things to do
besides give rides to penguins."

Ed quickly wrote
the message in the snow.

THANK YOU,
TALBOT.
BEST WISHES,
Ed

Then he climbed
on top of Ernest's back.
Ernest gave a couple of
big splashes with his tail,
and then they were racing
across the water.

"Ed is back!" yelled Betty.

"Hooray!" shouted Freddy and Al.

Ed slid off Ernest's back.
"Thanks a lot, Ernest," called Ed.

"That's O.K.," said Ernest.
"Just don't expect a ride every day."

"We're so glad you are back, Ed,"
said Betty.

"We missed you a lot,"
said Freddy and Al.

"I missed you," said Ed.

SPLAT! They were all soaked,
as Ernest swam away.

"Hey," said Betty, "he did it again!"

"Ernest doesn't notice penguins,"
said Freddy.

"Sometimes he does," said Ed.

Story Questions & Activities

1 How does Ed wind up alone?

2 How does Talbot help Ed?

3 What are some funny things that happen in the story? Why are they funny?

4 What is this story mostly about?

5 Imagine that Ed is forming a "Best Friends Club." Who would be in it and what kinds of rules might it have?

Write a Guide

Choose something you like to do and make a guide of "helpful hints" for someone who is learning to do the same thing. You can include both things that people have taught you and ideas of your own.

Create a Secret Message

Write a secret message. Dip a paintbrush in lemon juice. Then write on a piece of paper. After the paper dries, hold it near a light bulb. When the paper gets warm, the secret message will appear.

Where in the World?

Penguins live in only five places. With your class, find these places on a map or globe: Antarctica, Australia, New Zealand, South Africa, and the Galápagos Islands.

Find Out More

There is more than just one kind of penguin. Use an encyclopedia to find the names of at least three different types. Where is each penguin found? What is the average size of each kind?

Read an Encyclopedia

pen   Pennsylvania

Penguins

Penguins are birds that are not able to fly. But penguins can swim underwater. Their wings look like flippers, and their bodies are covered with short feathers. All penguins have black and white feathers. Some have stripes across their chests.

Penguins hatch their young from eggs

Penguins eat mostly fish. Penguins dive into the water to catch their food. They use their wings and their webbed feet to swim. Penguins live on islands near cold water in the southern part of the Earth.

Use the encyclopedia entry to answer the questions.

1 Where do penguins live?

2 What is the most surprising fact about penguins?

3 How do penguins swim?

4 How are encyclopedias and dictionaries alike? How are they different?

318

Read the story again if the questions seem too hard.

DIRECTIONS:
Read the story. Then read each question about the story.

SAMPLE

Never Too Old

In 1962, John Glenn was the first man from the United States to go into space. He went in a spaceship called *Friendship 7*.

He went around the Earth in *Friendship 7* three times. The trip took five hours. *Friendship 7* landed safely on the same day that it left. John Glenn was a hero.

In 1998, John Glenn went into space again. He was seventy-seven years old. He was the oldest man ever to go into space. He went in a spaceship called *Discovery*.

Discovery landed after nine days in space.

John Glenn was a hero again in 1998. He proved you are never too old to be a hero.

1 How old was John Glenn when he went into space in 1998?
○ Sixty-seven years old
○ Seventy-seven years old
○ Twenty-eight years old

2 John Glenn was a hero in 1962 because he —
○ went into space
○ walked on the moon
○ made friends in space

The Pony Express

Have you read the news?
Hurry! Spread the news!
The Pony Express is ahead!
A truck can send a letter
But a pony is much better.
The Pony Express is ahead!
Do you want to send your mail
But a truck is sure to fail?
Try a pony, instead!

Meet Dale Ryder

Dale Ryder is a writer who lives in New York City. Ryder has always been interested in the Pony Express. This is Ryder's first story for children.

Meet Kunio Hagio

When Kunio Hagio was growing up in Chicago, he knew he wanted to be an artist. But when he was 16, his right hand was so badly hurt in an accident that the doctors thought he'd never be able to draw again. Today he says, "There's nothing you can't overcome if you don't believe any reasons to quit." Kunio Hagio lives and works in Sedona, Arizona.

322

The Pony Express

Fastest Mail in the West

by Dale Ryder
Illustrated by Kunio Hagio

WANTED
EXPERT RIDERS
Under 125 Pounds

Must be tough,
loyal and honest
PONY EXPRESS

Young Johnnie Frye thought that described him pretty well. He signed up and became the first rider on the Pony Express.

The date was April 3, 1860. Before that day, it could take up to a month for mail to travel across the country. But the mail that left St. Joseph, Missouri, that day would arrive in San Francisco just ten days later. The Pony Express would be the fastest mail service ever.

An excited crowd gathered and watched as Johnnie put the special, very light saddle on his pony. Over the saddle lay a thin piece of leather called a *mochila*. *Mochila* is the Spanish word for knapsack. It had pockets in its four corners. The pockets, called *cantinas*, held the newspapers, letters, and telegrams that the Pony Express riders would take to California.

At 7:00 p.m. Johnnie set off. Everybody waved and cheered as he rushed away from them.

Johnnie rode on through the Missouri night. Every 10 to 12 miles he pulled up to a station to change horses. In less than two minutes, he threw the mochila onto the fresh horse and dashed off again.

Johnnie and his pony took a ferry across the Missouri River into Kansas. They sped across the flat prairie. Then, after 60 miles and eight hours of riding, Johnnie passed the mochila on to another rider.

New riders took over every 60 to 75 miles. They rode over the dusty plains, waded through rivers, and climbed over the rugged Rocky Mountains. They rode all day, west with the sun, and they rode all night, under dark, lonely skies.

327

The last rider on the route was William Hamilton. He pulled into Sacramento on April 13, and put the mail on a steamer ship for the quick run to San Francisco. The mail had been delivered in ten days as planned. In fact, it was two hours early!

At about the same time, there was a celebration in St. Joseph, Missouri. A Pony Express rider had just arrived there, ten days after leaving California. The Pony Express had kept its promise.

The Fastest Mail Ever

William H. Russell knew that many people had moved out west to California. There were no telegraph lines or railroad tracks that went all the way across the country at that time. But no one wanted to wait a month to get news from back home. Russell believed that horseback riders would be the fastest way to deliver mail to the West. Riders were much faster than stagecoaches.

Russell set to work. He built stations for switching horses all the way from St. Joseph to Sacramento. The stations were 10 to 12 miles apart. That was short enough for the horses to run between them at top speed.

Twenty-five of the 190 stations were called home stations. There the riders could rest at the end of their route. The 165 smaller "swing" stations were relay posts where the riders changed horses.

Russell now needed 400 horses. He bought fast, long-legged horses for going over flat land, and smaller, tough horses for the mountains. The horses of the Pony Express needed to be faster than most other horses, to keep the riders and the mail safe.

The regular Pony Express route was about 2000 miles. The riders started in Missouri, then went through Kansas. Finally, they rode along the Oregon Trail, passing through what is now Nebraska and Wyoming.

The most dangerous part of the Pony Express route was the Sierra Nevada Mountains. Mountain storms often covered the trail with snow. When the wind blew the snow into piles 10 feet high or more, a rider could go over a cliff. The rider had to know the trails well enough to find his way in any weather.

Those Daring Young Men

All the riders were a lot like Johnnie Frye—small, young men who had grown up riding over the mountains and the prairies. About 180 riders rode for the Express. Most were 19 or 20 years old, but at least one was as young as 11!

Word of the brave deeds of the Pony Express riders spread. They rode through storms and over flooded rivers. They were threatened by bandit attacks and buffalo stampedes. But the motto of the Pony Express was "The mail must go through!"—and it always did.

The Pony Express's work was very important. The letters and newspapers delivered by the riders helped keep the East and the West together. One rider, Bill Campbell, carried President Abraham Lincoln's Inaugural Address to the people of California.

Newspapers printed thrilling stories about the Pony Express riders. The young men became famous. Johnnie Frye, the first rider out of St. Joseph, was a real favorite. Many came out to watch him ride by. One story says that a woman invented the doughnut hole so that Johnnie could catch her cakes on his finger as he rode by!

The most famous rider was Bill Cody, later known as Buffalo Bill. He began riding for the Pony Express when he was only 15 years old.

Legend has it that on one trip there was no one to take over after Bill's ride. He had to ride another 76 miles to the next home station.

Before he could rest, the eastbound mail arrived. Bill took that mail and went back over his route. The entire trip, back and forth, was 384 miles. If this is true, Buffalo Bill holds the record for the longest Pony Express ride.

The Last Ride

But even though it was a success, the Pony Express would not last long. On October 24, 1861, the cross-country telegraph line was finished. Now a message could be sent across the country in minutes.

The last Pony Express rider handed over his mail pouch on November 21, 1861.

Although the Pony Express lasted only a year and a half, the riders became part of American legend. They had shown great daring and skill.

And it all started with Johnnie Frye, racing alone through that April night in 1860. He was proud to be part of the Pony Express. He knew that it was up to him to make sure that the mail went through. And it did.

THE PONY EXPRESS
1860-1861

THE MAIL MUST GET THROUGH

Story Questions & Activities

1. What was the Pony Express?

2. Why did the riders for the Pony Express have to be under 125 pounds?

3. What did the Pony Express riders like about their work?

4. What is the main idea of this selection?

5. Would José from "Roundup at Rio Ranch" be a good rider for the Pony Express? Why or why not?

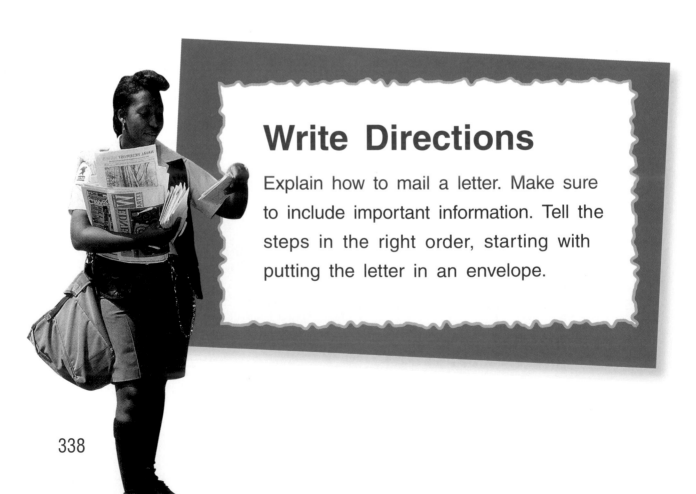

Write Directions

Explain how to mail a letter. Make sure to include important information. Tell the steps in the right order, starting with putting the letter in an envelope.

Make a Map of the Pony Express

Trace the outline of a map of the United States. Then find, mark, and label one of the places mentioned in "The Pony Express." You might look for St. Joseph, Missouri, or the Rocky Mountains, or San Francisco, California.

Make a Collage

The Pony Express helped news travel quickly between East and West. How do people get mail and news now? Draw or cut out pictures of things people use to get mail. Make a collage that shows these inventions.

Find Out More

The cross-country telegraph caused the end of the Pony Express. What is the telegraph? Who invented it? How long did it take to get messages?

Use a Telephone Directory

The white pages list the phone numbers of people.

96 Jagoda–Jenson

Jagoda Nadine F 13 West 25th St 878-1315
Jaime Raul 20 Christopher St 715-2596
Jamison Andrew 16 East 16th St 878-6945
Jamison Andrew 40 Maidstone Ln 605-7344

The yellow pages list the phone numbers of businesses.

30 Coin Dealers–Computer Dealers
Coin Dealers

Murray's Rare Coins 1 University Pl 949-9142
Stone's Coin Co. 40 Bedford St 654-6087
Comic Books

Comic Vault 424 East 3rd St 805-3984
Quick Comics 60 Brook Rd 716-4747
Computer Dealers

The Computer Cave 222 2nd Ave 493-2180

1 What is the phone number of Quick Comics?

2 What is the address of Stone's Coin Co.?

3 Why do you think phone directories include addresses?

4 How are the white pages and the yellow pages of a phone book different?

340

TEST POWER

Think about why the characters act the way they do.

DIRECTIONS:

Read the story. Then read each question about the story.

SAMPLE

The Boy Who Cried Wolf

Long ago, a boy lived on a sheep farm. His job was to keep the sheep safe. The farmers told him to yell if he saw a wolf. Wolves would eat the sheep.

One day, the boy was bored. He wanted to have some fun. He yelled, "Help! I see a wolf."

The farmers heard him. They ran to help. When they got to the boy, he laughed, "There is no wolf. I was playing a joke." The farmers were angry.

The next day a wolf crept out of the woods. "Help!" yelled the boy. "A wolf is eating the sheep." The farmers heard the boy but did not go to him. They all thought that he was playing another joke.

1 Why didn't the farmers run to help the boy?
- ● They did not believe him.
- ○ They did not hear him.
- ○ They were sleeping.

2 Which is a FACT from this story?
- ● The boy played a joke.
- ○ The farmers played a joke.
- ○ The sheep played a joke.

Tiger's Friends

Tiger, tiger, shining brightly
Saw a monkey skipping lightly.
"Oh, happy monkey, where are
    you going?"
"I'm taking my friend Donkey rowing."
"May I please come?" the tiger
    asked sweetly,
"If your boat can hold three neatly?"
"Of course you may," said the monkey.
"Let's go and get my friend Donkey.
Then how happy we will be,
Monkey, donkey, and tiger at sea!"

A FOLK TALE FROM THE HMONG PEOPLE OF LAOS
TOLD BY BLIA XIONG

NINE ▸ IN ▸ ONE, GRR! GRR!

ADAPTED BY CATHY SPAGNOLI
ILLUSTRATED BY NANCY HOM

Many years ago when the earth was nearer the sky than it is today, there lived the first tiger. She and her mate had no babies and so the lonely tiger often thought about the future, wondering how many cubs she would have.

Tiger decided to visit the great god Shao, who lived in the sky, who was kind and gentle and knew everything. Surely Shao could tell her how many cubs she would have.

Tiger set out on the road that led to the sky. She climbed through forests of striped bamboo and wild banana trees, past plants curved like rooster tail feathers, and over rocks shaped like sleeping dragons.

At last Tiger came to a stone wall. Beyond the wall was a garden where children played happily under a plum tree. A large house stood nearby, its colorful decorations shining in the sun. This was the land of the great Shao, a peaceful land without sickness or death.

Shao himself came out to greet Tiger. The silver coins dangling from his belt sounded softly as he walked.

"Why did you come here, Tiger?" he asked gently.

"O great Shao," answered Tiger respectfully, "I am lonely and want to know how many cubs I will have."

Shao was silent for a moment. Then he replied, "Nine each year."

"How wonderful," purred Tiger. "Thank you so much, great Shao." And she turned to leave with her good news.

"One moment, Tiger," said Shao. "You must remember carefully what I said. The words alone tell you how many cubs you will have. Do not forget them, for if you do, I cannot help you."

At first Tiger was happy as she followed the road back to earth. But soon, she began to worry.

"Oh dear," she said to herself. "My memory is so bad. How will I ever remember those important words of Shao?" She thought and she thought. At last, she had an idea. "I'll make up a little song to sing. Then I won't forget." So Tiger began to sing:

Nine-in-one, Grr! Grr!
Nine-in-one, Grr! Grr!

Down the mountain went Tiger, past the rocks shaped like sleeping dragons, past the plants curved like rooster tail feathers, through the forests of striped bamboo and wild banana trees. Over and over she sang her song:

Nine-in-one, Grr! Grr!
Nine-in-one, Grr! Grr!

As Tiger came closer to her cave, she passed through clouds of tiny white butterflies. She heard monkeys and barking deer. She saw green-striped snakes, quails and pheasants. None of the animals listened to her song—except one big, clever, black bird, the Eu bird.

"Hmm," said Bird to herself. "I wonder why Tiger is coming down the mountain singing that song and grinning from ear to ear. I'd better find out." So Bird soared up the ladder which was a shortcut to Shao's home.

"**O** wise Shao," asked Bird politely, "why is Tiger singing over and over:

Nine-in-one, Grr! Grr!
Nine-in-one, Grr! Grr!

And Shao explained that he had just told Tiger she would have nine cubs each year.

"That's terrible!" squawked Bird. "If Tiger has nine cubs each year, they will eat all of us. Soon there will be nothing but tigers in the land. You must change what you said, O Shao!"

"I cannot take back my words," sighed Shao. "I promised Tiger that she would have nine cubs every year as long as she remembered my words."

"As long as she remembered your words," repeated Bird thoughtfully. "Then I know what I must do, O great Shao."

Bird now had a plan. She could hardly wait to try it out. Quickly, she returned to earth in search of Tiger.

Bird reached her favorite tree as old grandmother sun was setting, just in time to hear Tiger coming closer and closer and still singing:

Nine-in-one, Grr! Grr!
Nine-in-one, Grr! Grr!

Tiger was concentrating so hard on her song that she didn't even see Bird landing in the tree above her.

Suddenly, Bird began to flap her wings furiously. "Flap! Flap! Flap!" went Bird's big, black wings.

"Who's that?" cried Tiger.

"It's only me," answered Bird innocently.

Tiger looked up and growled at Bird:

"Grr! Grr! Bird. You made me forget my song with all your noise."

"h, I can help you," chirped Bird sweetly. "I heard you walking through the woods. You were singing:

One-in-nine, Grr! Grr!
One-in-nine, Grr! Grr!

"Oh, thank you, thank you, Bird!" cried Tiger. "I will have one cub every nine years. How wonderful! This time I won't forget!"

So Tiger returned to her cave, singing happily:

One-in-nine, Grr! Grr!
One-in-nine, Grr! Grr!

And that is why, the Hmong people say, we don't have too many tigers on the earth today!

MEET BLIA XIONG ◄

Blia Xiong (BLEE-AH SHONG) first heard *Nine-in-One, Grr! Grr!* when she was a little child. She says, "This story was carried in my family for a long time. I was three when I first heard it. I still remember my mother telling me this funny story with a tiger singing in Laotian, 'Nine-in-One, Grr! Grr!'"

In Laos, the tiger is a wild animal that is feared. Some people think the tiger is magical. She says, "The part I like most is when the bird hears the song and figures out how to trick the tiger. The clever bird does something about the powerful tiger."

Blia Xiong was told stories by her mother, her father, and her grandfather before them. Now she tells her children the stories she hears. When asked how she remembers a story, she says, "When I listen to a story, I listen very closely. I make pictures in my mind. Then I can remember what I hear."

MEET NANCY HOM ►

Nancy Hom was born in southern China and grew up in New York City. In addition to *Nine-in-One, Grr! Grr!* she has illustrated the Cambodian folk tale *Judge Rabbit and the Tree Spirit*.

Story Questions & Activities

1. Why does Tiger visit the great Shao?

2. Why does Bird want to make Tiger forget her song?

3. What are some things Tiger does in the story that real tigers do not do?

4. What is this story mostly about?

5. Compare the illustrations in this story to the illustrations in "Luka's Quilt." How are the pictures different? How are they alike?

Write a Report

The tiger in this story will teach her children how to be good tigers. Choose an animal you like. What do you know about that kind of animal? What do you like about it? What would it teach its children?

Multiplying Tigers

In the story, Tiger wonders how many cubs she will have. If Tiger has one cub every nine years, how many cubs will she have in 18 years?

The Biggest Cat in the World

The Siberian tiger can grow up to 4 feet tall and over 9 feet long. And that does not include its tail! Work together to make a life-size drawing of a Siberian tiger. Use a large piece of paper and a ruler.

Find Out More

Go to the library to find another story or folk tale about a tiger. What country does the story come from? Read it. Then write down your favorite part of the story.

Use a Dictionary

ticket/tight

ticket   A card or piece of paper that gives the person who holds it the right to be admitted or to get a service. You need a *ticket* to ride the train.
     tick•et (TIHK it) *noun, plural* **tickets**.

tickle   To touch people in a way that makes them laugh. It makes me laugh when someone *tickles* my feet.
     tick•le (TIHK uhl) *verb,* **tickled, tickling**.

tiger   A large, powerful animal that is a member of the cat family. Most tigers have an orange or yellow coat with black or brown stripes. Tigers live in Asia. We saw *tigers* at the zoo.
     ti•ger (TĪ guhr) *noun, plural* **tigers.**

Use the part of a dictionary page to answer the questions.

1 What is the meaning of the word *tiger?*

2 Why does *tickle* come between *ticket* and *tiger?*

3 What part of speech is the word *ticket?*

4 What is the example sentence for *tickle?*

TEST POWER

Think about the story as you read it.

DIRECTIONS:
Read the story. Then read each question about the story.

SAMPLE

The Garden

Each morning, the sun comes up. The birds in the garden start to sing. The wet grass starts to dry. The crickets and grasshoppers get to work. They wash the dishes. They sweep the floor. The ants put on their glasses to look closely at the flowers. The ladybugs polish the leaves with rags. All day the insects work to make the garden beautiful. At the end of the day, everyone but the crickets climbs into bed. The crickets have one more job. They will make music for the others in the garden.

1 Why does the grass start to dry?
- ○ The sun shines on it.
- ○ The crickets and grasshoppers hop through it.
- ○ The ants look at it closely.

2 How do you know this story is make-believe?
- ○ Insects don't live in the garden.
- ○ There are no such things as ladybugs.
- ○ Ants don't wear glasses.

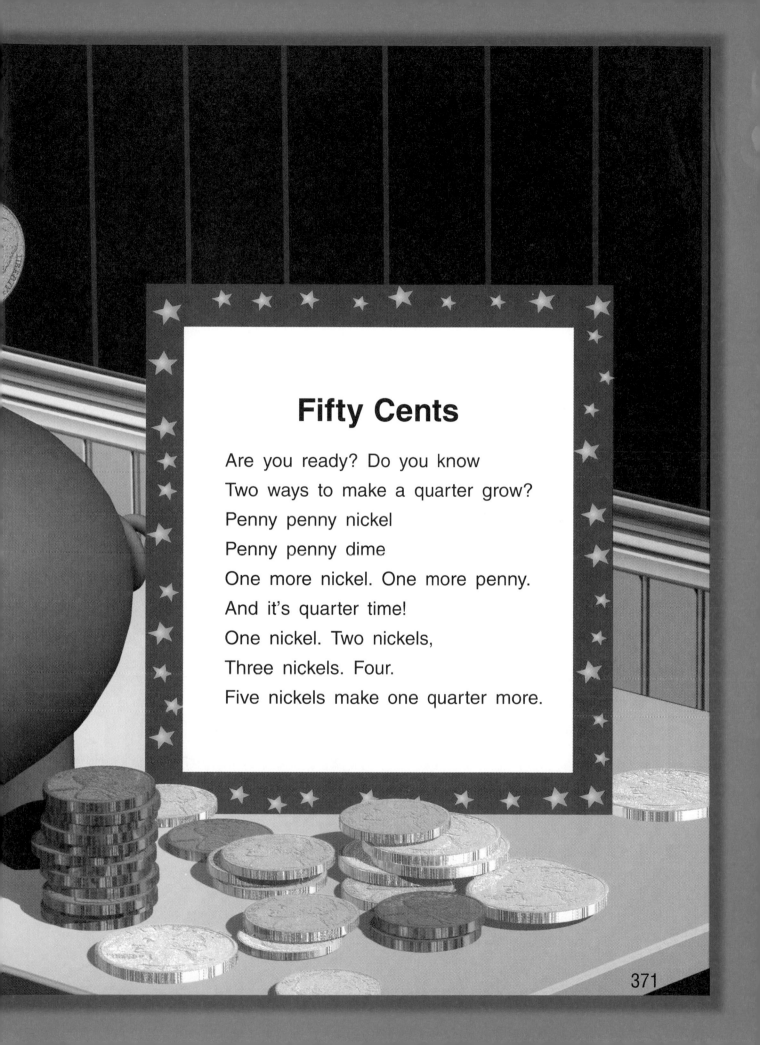

Fifty Cents

Are you ready? Do you know
Two ways to make a quarter grow?
Penny penny nickel
Penny penny dime
One more nickel. One more penny.
And it's quarter time!
One nickel. Two nickels,
Three nickels. Four.
Five nickels make one quarter more.

TIME FOR KIDS

SPECIAL REPORT

Change for the QUARTER

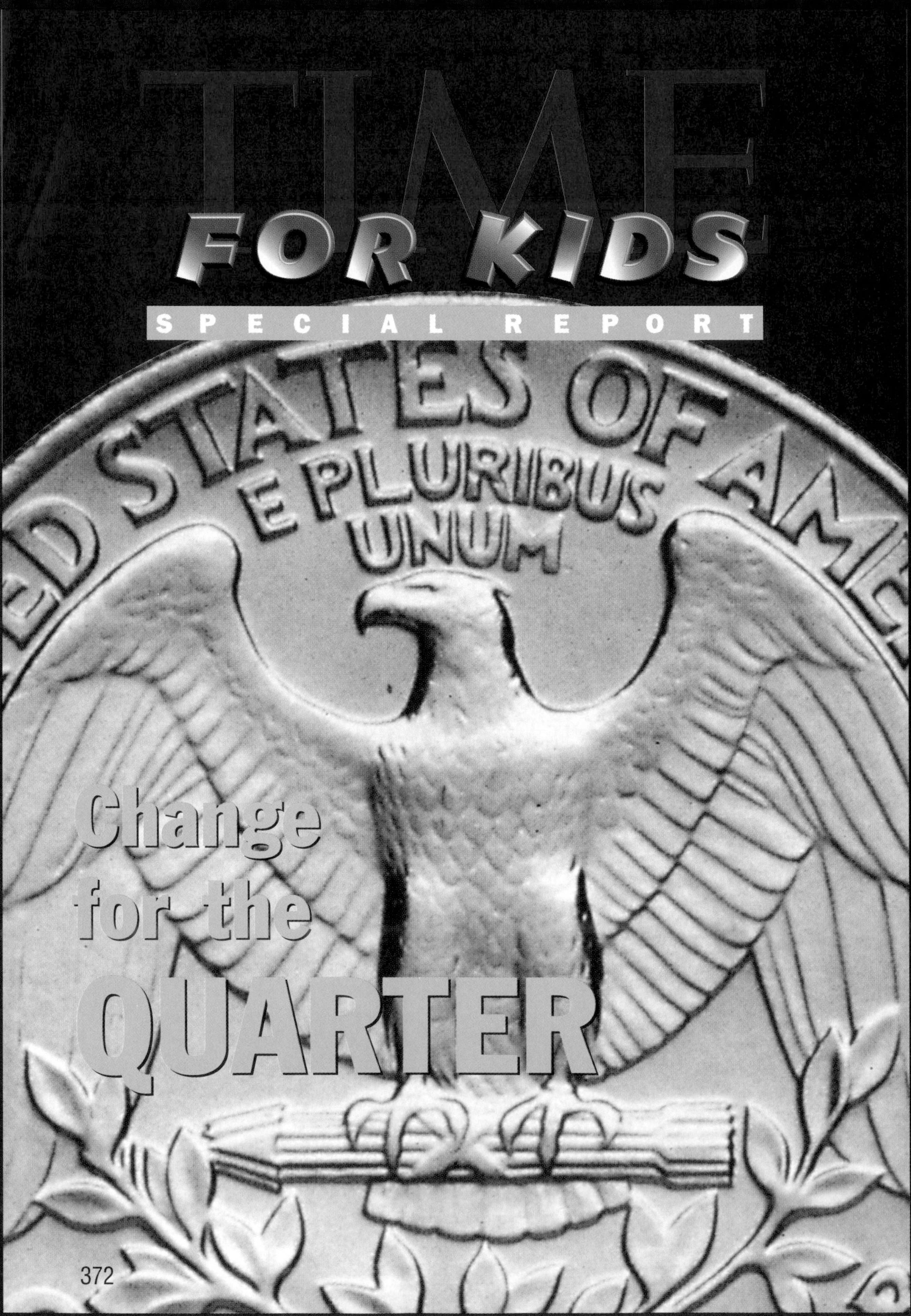
ED STATES OF AME
E PLURIBUS
UNUM

Delaware

New Jersey

Pennsylvania

Georgia

Connecticut

THIS PAGE AND COVER: COURTESY, U.S. MINT

Quarters Get a New Look

The change in your pocket is changing. At least, the quarter is. The 25-cent piece is getting a new look. The eagle on the back side is going away. In its place, there will be 50 new designs. (George Washington is staying on the "heads" side.)

Each of the 50 new designs honors a state. Each year for 10 years, five new quarters will be made. States will be honored in the order they joined the United States.

The first new quarters have already come out. You may have seen them by now. They honor the states of Connecticut, Delaware, Georgia, New Jersey, and Pennsylvania.

George Washington is still with us!

373

Some people collect coins from around the world.

They were the first five states to join the United States. So they were the first of the 50 states to be honored with new quarters. You'll get to see the last five state quarters in 2008.

Kids love the idea. "It's nice to have a change," says Shannon Vinson, from Baltimore, Maryland. "I'll collect all 50 for show-and-tell."

That's just what the U.S. government wants. Quarters are made for just a few cents. But they are worth 25 cents when you use them. If people keep the coins instead of spending them, the government will get to keep the difference. It could add up to more than $5 billion. Not exactly small change!

The First States

Below is a list of the first 10 states to join the U.S. Is your state one of them? If not, find out when your state became a state. And start watching your change. You might be holding a quarter with your state's special picture on it.

The First 10 States	When Each Became a State
Delaware	December 7, 1787
Pennsylvania	December 12, 1787
New Jersey	December 18, 1787
Georgia	January 2, 1788
Connecticut	January 9, 1788
Massachusetts	February 6, 1788
Maryland	April 28, 1788
South Carolina	May 23, 1788
New Hampshire	June 21, 1788
Virginia	June 25, 1788

Smart State

Look at the list. One state is 15 days older than the state after it. But the two states joined the U.S. in different years. What states are they? (Hint: One state starts with the letter N. The other state begins with the letter G.)

Eagle quarters won't be made again until all 50 states have a coin of their own.

FIND OUT MORE

Visit our website:

www.mhschool.com/reading

*inter*NET
CONNECTION

Based on an article in *TIME FOR KIDS*.

Story Questions & Activities

1 Which side of the quarter is changing?

2 Why does the U.S. government hope that people will collect the new quarters?

3 How do the new quarters honor different states?

4 What is the main idea of this selection?

5 If you designed money to honor the land of Shao, from "Nine-in-One Grr! Grr!", what might it look like and why?

Write a How-To Article

Is there something that you collect or would like to collect? Write an article for a magazine about collecting. Explain how someone can start his or her own collection. Give three steps to follow.

Make a Guess

If you flipped a quarter 40 times, how many times do you think it would come up heads? Tails? Write your guess. Then flip a quarter 40 times. Make a chart that compares how many times you get heads and how many times you get tails.

??????????????????????????????????????

Design Your Own Quarter

Think about what is special about your state. Then design a quarter that honors your state. Draw pictures for the front and the back.

Find Out More

Look on the "tails" side of a penny, a nickel, a dime. What pictures are there? Learn more about the designs. What are they? What do they mean?

Choose a Reference Source

Dictionary

mint¹ 1. A plant that has fragrant leaves that are used as flavoring and in medicine. Peppermint and spearmint are kinds of mint. **2.** A candy flavored with mint.
   mint (mint) *noun, plural* **mints**.

mint² 1. A place where metal is made into coins. **2.** A large amount of money. *A fancy car like that must cost a mint. Noun.* **3.** To make coins. *The government minted new quarters this year. Verb.*
   mint (mint) *noun, plural* **mints**; *verb,* **minted**, **minting**.

Encyclopedia

Mint A mint is a place where coins are made. In most countries, only the government can make coins. The United States has mints in Denver, Philadelphia, San Francisco, and West Point, New York.

   The first mint in the world was built during the 600's B.C. This mint was in Lydia, which is now part of Turkey.

Mint Most people think of the flavor of peppermint when they hear the word *mint*. But actually, mint is the name of a family of plants. Their leaves have a pleasant smell. Mint grows in all parts of the world.

Choose a reference to answer each question.

1 Which book tells you where mints are located in the United States?

2 Which book gives you all the different meanings of the word *mint*?

3 When was the first mint built? Which book did you use to find your answer?

4 How are a dictionary and an encyclopedia alike? How are they different?

TEST POWER

A FACT is something that is true in the story.

DIRECTIONS:
Read the story. Then read each question about the story.

SAMPLE

A Trip to the Museum

Biu woke up on Monday morning. She looked at her clock. It read nine o'clock. "Oh, no," she thought, "I'm late for school." She ran out of her bedroom and yelled, "Dad, I'm late." Her dad said, "It's the first day of vacation." Biu let out a sigh of relief.

Biu got dressed and went into the kitchen. Her father was staring out the window.

"Good morning," he said. "What a wet day it is."

Biu asked, "Any ideas for a fun day inside?" "How about a trip to the museum?" he asked. Biu loved going to the art museum. Biu said happily, "That sounds great!"

1 Why was Biu worried when she woke up late?
○ She thought she was late for school.
○ She thought she was late for a visit to the doctor.
○ She thought it was Sunday.

2 Which is a FACT from this story?
○ Biu liked going to art museums.
○ Biu liked going to school.
○ Biu is a boy.

Time to Play

Mama says to play outside.
Wish I had a bike to ride.
I'll fly to the moon instead.
Steer the rocket in my head.
I'll pretend to find a star
no one else has seen so far.
Then I'll name it after me—
        Africa Lawanda Lee!
But for now I'll grab some chalk,
play hopscotch out on the walk.

by Nikki Grimes

Reading for

You get information from many sources such as television, newspapers, advertisements, and the Internet. In school, textbooks bring you information about different subjects. In this section, you will learn strategies to help you understand and use the many kinds of information that are a part of your everyday life.

Information

Contents

Reading Social Studies

Reading Directions

Reading Media

Reading Social Studies

A social studies book gives information about people and places. Learning how to read a social studies book will help you to understand it better. The tips below will help you to be a careful reader.

Preview, Ask, Read, Review

1 **Preview the article.** Read the titles and captions. Look at the pictures. What is the article about?

2 **Ask questions** before you read. For example: "What will I learn from this article?"

3 **Read and reread.** Reread any sentences that you don't understand. Look up any words that you don't know.

4 **Review, or think about,** what you have read. Did you find the answers to your questions?

①

Preview.
The title and pictures tell me this will be a story about milk.

②

Ask questions.
I think about questions like this one as I read.

③

Read and reread.
I match each step with the pictures.

④

Review.
The answer to this question will help me remember how milk gets to the market.

How does milk get to the market?

You drink milk every day. Milk comes from a cow. How does it get to your table?

1. The farmer uses a machine to milk the cow.

2. A truck driver takes the milk to the dairy plant.

3. At the plant, people put the milk into bottles or cartons.

4. A truck driver takes the milk to the market.

How many people help to get the milk from the farm to the market?

GEOGRAPHY SKILLS

Main Idea

Maps have parts that help us to understand them.

Using Maps

What is a map?

A **map** is a drawing of a place. This picture shows what a neighborhood looks like from above. The map on the next page is a drawing of the same neighborhood. How are the picture and the map alike?

What is a symbol?

Many maps have **symbols**. A symbol is a picture that stands for something else. Symbols on a map may be shapes, colors, or pictures. What symbols do you see on this map?

What is a map key?

A **map key** tells what the symbols on a map mean. Find the map key. What symbol stands for a pool? How many symbols are on this map key?

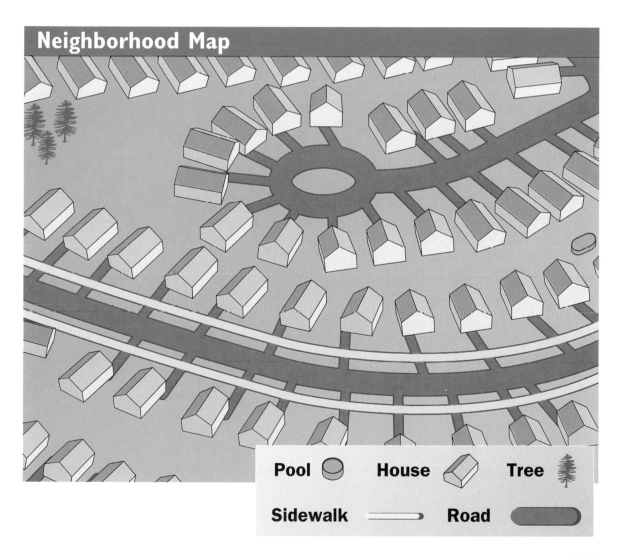

Neighborhood Map

| Pool | ⬭ | House | ⬦ | Tree | 🌲 |
| Sidewalk | ⎯⎯▷ | Road | ▬▬ | | |

GEOGRAPHY SKILLS

What can a map show?

Maps can show different things. Some maps show neighborhoods or cities. Some show land and water.

This is a map of the United States. The United States is a **country**. A country is a land and the people who live there. This map shows the **states** in our country.

What is the name of your state? Find it on the map.
Name a state that looks bigger than your state.

Review Questions

1. What does a map key tell you?
2. What are some things you can find on a map?
3. Why do social studies books have maps in them?

THE UNITED STATES

Reading Directions

Learning how to read directions is an important skill. Directions tell you how to make or do something, step by step. Directions may include a title, a list of supplies that you will need, steps to follow, and a picture or diagram.

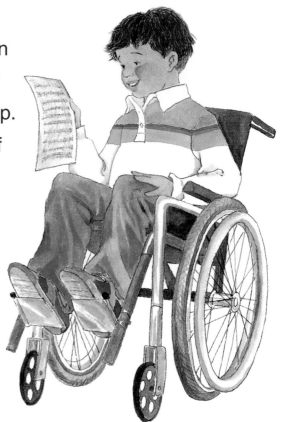

Directions have
a title
materials
steps to follow
pictures

How to Read Directions

① **Read through the steps before you begin.** You can make sure you have everything you will need.

② **Look up words** you don't know.

③ **Reread the steps.** This will tell you what to do next.

④ **Do each step in order.** Don't skip or mix up any steps. If you do, your project may not work!

1. **Read all of the steps.** I will gather my materials before I begin.

2. **Look up words.** I will check the word *occasionally* in step 3.

3. **Read the steps again.** I need to put the food coloring in the water first.

4. **Do each step in order.** I won't see the dots until the celery is cut.

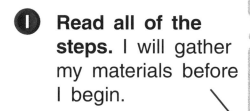

Colorful Flowers

You can make a colored flower to see how a plant uses water.

What you need

- a white flower
- a stalk of celery
- a glass of water
- blue food coloring

What to do

1. Add 2 drops of food coloring to the water.
2. Stand the flower and the celery in the blue water.
3. Wait an hour. Check the flower and celery occasionally.
4. Watch them change color as water moves up the stems.
5. Ask an adult to cut the celery in half. You will see blue dots where the water moved up the stem.

Paper Bag Puppets

Do you have an extra lunch bag? Use these directions to turn it into a bird puppet.

Materials

- plain paper lunch bag
- safety scissors
- construction paper
- markers
- paste or glue
- feathers (optional)

Directions

1. Lay the paper bag flat on the table.The flap should be at the top and facing you.

2. Cut two triangles from construction paper for the beak. Glue one triangle to the top flap on the lower edge.

3. Lift the flap up. Glue the other triangle on the bag so it is right under the first triangle.

4. From construction paper, cut out eyes, head feathers, and wings. Glue them to the body of your puppet.

5. Cut out paper feathers or use real feathers. Glue them to the back for a tail.

6. To work your puppet, put your hand inside. Curl your fingers into the flap. Move your fingers to open and close the mouth.

Review Questions

1. What is the first step?
2. When do you make the tail?
3. Why is it important to know how to read directions?

Reading Media

People can get information from newspapers, billboards, television, and magazines. They are all examples of *media*. To better understand media, think about how each form is alike and different. The chart below will help you to do this.

Media	Print	Pictures	Sound
Television	●	●	●
Billboard	●	●	
Newspaper	●	●	
Magazine	●	●	

Comparing Forms of Information

1. **Preview the media.** Identify what kinds of media they are.

2. **Look at how each kind of media gives information.** How are they alike? Which ones use print? color? pictures? sound?

3. **Look for differences.** Find ways that each kind of media is different.

4. **Think about what you have learned.** What new information did you learn from comparing different kinds of media?

Billboards and Newspapers

A billboard is a large outdoor sign. It uses print and pictures to get our attention.

A newspaper is printed on sheets of paper. It contains up-to-date news, pictures, and advertisements.

❶ Preview the media. The two different kinds of media here are a billboard and a newspaper.

Weekly Gazette

SEAT BELTS SAVE FAMILY!

Buckle Up!
Seat belts Save Lives!

❷ Look at each kind of media. Both the billboard and newspaper use print and pictures.

❸ Think about what you learned. A newspaper and a billboard can provide the same information in different ways.

❹ Look for differences. The billboard is much larger than the newspaper.

Television

Television uses moving pictures, sound, and print. Sometimes television sells a product. Sometimes television gives us information. How are a billboard and television alike?

Magazines

A magazine uses pictures and words. Sometimes a magazine gives us information. Sometimes it sells a product or idea.

I wear a mask and pads when I play. I know it's smart to be safe.

I wear a seat belt when I drive. It's always smart to be safe.

Review Questions

1. Look at the television screen and the magazine page. How is the information that we get from them alike?

2. What is different about the information?

3. Why is it important to know how to compare different kinds of media?

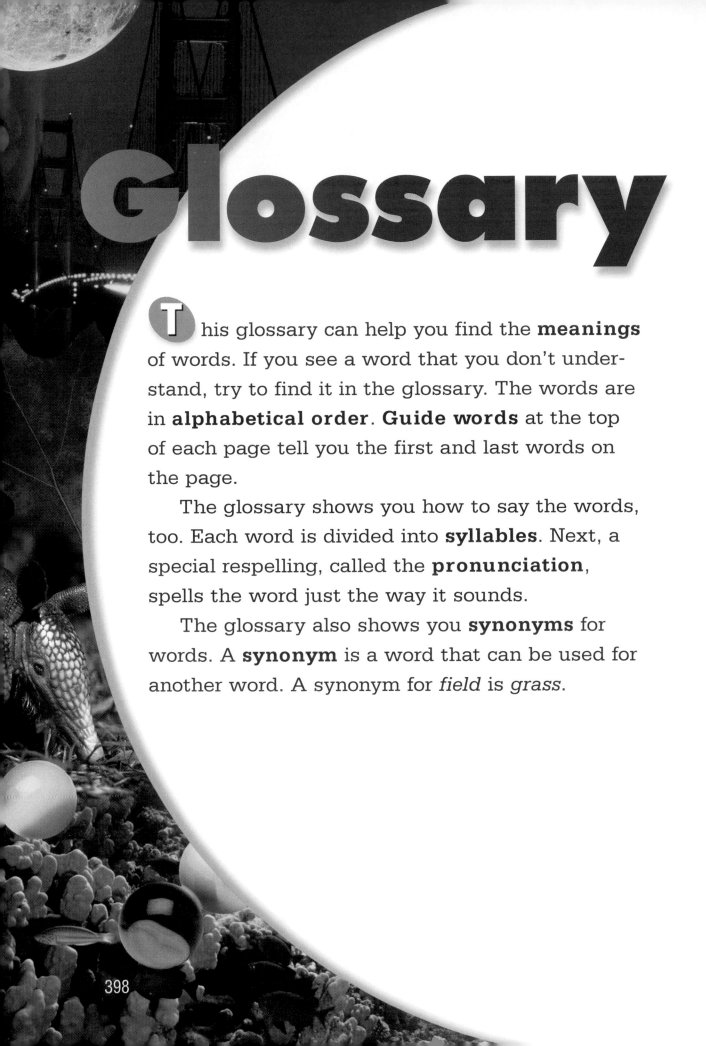

Glossary

This glossary can help you find the **meanings** of words. If you see a word that you don't understand, try to find it in the glossary. The words are in **alphabetical order**. **Guide words** at the top of each page tell you the first and last words on the page.

The glossary shows you how to say the words, too. Each word is divided into **syllables**. Next, a special respelling, called the **pronunciation**, spells the word just the way it sounds.

The glossary also shows you **synonyms** for words. A **synonym** is a word that can be used for another word. A synonym for *field* is *grass*.

accident / binoculars

First word on the page   Last word on the page

Sample Entry

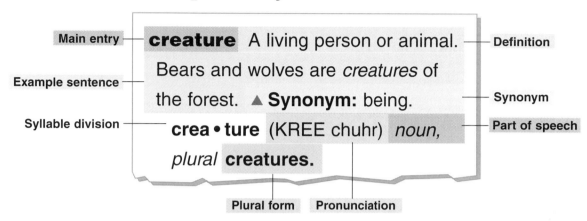

Main entry — **creature** A living person or animal. — Definition

Example sentence — Bears and wolves are *creatures* of the forest. ▲ **Synonym:** being. — Synonym

Syllable division — crea•ture (KREE chuhr) *noun,* — Part of speech

plural **creatures.**

Plural form   Pronunciation

Use the **Pronunciation Key** below to find examples for the sounds you see in the **pronunciation** spellings.

Phonetic Spelling	Examples	Phonetic Spelling	Examples
a	cat	oh	go, home
ah	father	aw	saw, fall
ay	late, day	or	more, four
air	there, hair	oo	too, do
b	bit, rabbit	oy	toy
ch	chin	ow	out, cow
d	dog	p	pig
e	met	r	run, carry
ee	he, see	s	song, mess
f	fine, off	sh	shout, fish
g	go, bag, bigger	t	ten, better
h	hat	th	thin
hw	wheel	thh	them
ih	sit	u	sun
ī	fine, tiger, my	u̇	look, should
ihr	near, deer, here	yoo	music, new
j	jump, page	ur	turn, learn
k	cat, back	v	very, of
l	line, hill	w	we
m	mine, hammer	y	yes
n	nice, funny	z	has, zoo
ng	sing	zh	treasure, division
o	top	uh	about, happen, lemon

Aa

afraid Feeling fear. Are you *afraid* of snakes?
> **a•fraid** (uh FRAYD) *adjective.*

allow To let someone do something. Tod and Teri's parents sometimes *allow* them to stay up later on Saturday nights.
> **al•low** (uh LOW) *verb,* **allowed, allowing.**

announce To make something known in an official or formal way. The principal *announced* that the school would be closed because of snow.
> ▲ **Synonyms:** report, proclaim.
> **an•nounce** (uh NOWNS) *verb,* **announced, announcing.**

answer To speak or write, as a reply. We *answer* people when they ask us a question, or call us, or send us a letter.
> ▲ **Synonym:** respond.
> **an•swer** (AN suhr) *verb,* **answered, answering.**

arrive To come to a place. We will *arrive* in Florida at midnight.
> **ar•rive** (uh RĪV) *verb,* **arrived, arriving.**

artist 1. A person who is skilled in painting, music, literature, or any other form of art. **2.** A person whose work shows talent or skill. The cook at this restaurant is an *artist.*
> **art•ist** (AHR tihst) *noun,* *plural* **artists.**

Bb

bamboo A tall, woody plant related to grass. He waved a *bamboo* cane.
> **bam•boo** (bam BOO) *noun,* *plural* **bamboo.**

Berto (BUR toh)

body 1. The whole of a person, animal, or plant. An athlete must have a strong *body*. **2.** The main part of something. The *body* of this car needs work.

　bod•y (BAHD ee) *noun, plural* **bodies.**

broken 1. In pieces. The *broken* plate could not be fixed. **2.** Not working. We took the *broken* television set back to the store to be fixed.

　▲ **Synonyms:** shattered, ruined.
　bro•ken (BROH kuhn) *adjective.*

buffalo A large North American animal that has a big shaggy head with short horns and a hump on its back; bison. We saw a herd of *buffalo* while traveling out West.

　buf•fa•lo (BUF uh loh) *noun, plural* **buffaloes** or **buffalos** or **buffalo.**

building Something built to live, work, or do things in. The *building* across the street is very tall.

　build•ing (BIHL ding) *noun, plural* **buildings.**

bully A person who likes to frighten or threaten others, especially smaller or weaker people. The cowardly *bully* picked only on younger children.

　bul•ly (BUL ee) *noun, plural* **bullies.**

busy Doing something. Roberta can't play because she is *busy* doing her homework.

　▲ **Synonyms:** active, occupied.
　bus•y (BIHZ ee) *adjective,* **busier, busiest.**

Cc

candle A wax stick with a string through it that is burned to make a light. The family lit eight *candles* on the last night of Hanukkah.

can•dle (KAN duhl) *noun, plural* **candles.**

careful Paying attention to what you are doing. Tina is very *careful* not to spill the paint. She works *carefully*.

▲ **Synonym:** cautious.
care•ful (KAIR fuhl) *adjective;* **carefully,** *adverb.*

carrot A long, orange vegetable that grows in the ground. The root of the plant is the part that we eat. Alice sliced a *carrot* for the salad.

car•rot (KAR uht) *noun, plural* **carrots.**

cattle Large animals raised for milk and meat on dairy farms and ranches. The *cattle* are grazing in the field.

▲ **Synonyms:** cows, bulls.
cat•tle (KAT uhl) *noun, plural* **cattle.**

chew To crush or grind something with the teeth. It's important to *chew* food well.

chew (CHOO) *verb,* **chewed, chewing.**

climb To move up something. Mom had to *climb* a ladder to get the kite out of the tree.

▲ **Synonym:** ascend.
climb (KLĪM) *verb,* **climbed, climbing.**

collect To gather together. The campers *collected* wood for the fire.
▲ **Synonym:** accumulate, amass.
col•lect (kuh LEKT) *verb,* **collected, collecting.**

corner The place where two streets come together. Paul crossed at the *corner.*
cor•ner (KOR nur) *noun,* *plural* **corners.**

couple Two things that go together in some way; a pair. I have a *couple* of hats.
cou•ple (KUP uhl) *noun,* *plural* **couples.**

crawl To move slowly on your hands and knees. The baby is just beginning to learn to *crawl.*
crawl (KRAWL) *verb,* **crawled, crawling.**

Dd

danger The chance that something bad will happen. There is *danger* in skating on thin ice.
danger (DAYN juhr) *noun,* *plural* **dangers.**

decide To choose to do one thing and not another. Carlos may *decide* not to go.
▲ **Synonym:** resolve.
de•cide (dih SĪD) *verb,* **decided, deciding.**

difference The amount left over. The *difference* between 6 and 2 is 4.
dif•fer•ence (DIHF uhr ens) *noun, plural* **differences.**

different Not the same. A duck is *different* from a goose.
dif•fer•ent (DIHF uhr ent) *adjective.*

diver A person who works or explores underwater. The *diver* carried a tank of air to help him breathe underwater.

div•er (DĪV uhr) *noun, plural* **divers.**

drift To move because of a current of air or water. We stopped rowing and let our boat *drift*.

▲ **Synonyms:** wander, float.

drift (DRIHFT) *verb,* **drifted, drifting.**

early 1. In or near the beginning. We started our hike in the *early* morning. **2.** Before the usual time. We had an *early* dinner.

ear•ly (UR lee) *adjective,* **earlier, earliest;** *adverb.*

Earth The planet we live on. It takes one year for the *Earth* to go around the sun.

Earth (URTH) *noun.*

edge The line or place where something ends. I live near the *edge* of the lake.

edge (EJ) *noun, plural* **edges.**

empty Having nothing in it. When I finished my soup, the bowl was *empty*.

emp•ty (EMP tee) *adjective,* **emptier, emptiest.**

famous Very well-known. Thomas Edison is *famous* for having invented the electric light.

fa•mous (FAY muhs) *adjective.*

fence That which is built around something to keep things out or in. The *fence* around our backyard keeps the dog in.

fence (FENS) *noun, plural* **fences.**

finish 1. To bring to an end; to complete. When we *finish* our work, we will have lunch. *Verb.* 2. The last part of something; the end. We stayed to the *finish* of the movie. *Noun.*

fin•ish (FIHN ihsh) *verb,* **finished, finishing;** *noun, plural* **finishes.**

float 1. To stay on top of the water. Ray has a toy boat that *floats.* 2. To move slowly in the air. The baby let the balloon go, and it *floated* high above the house.

▲ **Synonym:** drift.

float (FLOHT) *verb,* **floated, floating.**

forget To not remember something. Josie was afraid she would *forget* my address, so she wrote it down.

▲ **Synonyms:** overlook, neglect.

for•get (fur GET) *verb,* **forgot, forgotten** or **forgot, forgetting.**

form To make or shape something. The artist *formed* a cat out of clay.

form (FORM) *verb,* **formed, forming.**

garden A place where people grow flowers or vegetables. When our cousins visit, they always bring us fresh tomatoes from their *garden.*

gar•den (GAHR duhn) *noun, plural* **gardens.**

gentle Careful not to hurt someone or something. Trisha was *gentle* with the small puppy.

▲ **Synonym:** soft.

gen•tle (JEN tuhl) *adjective.*

405

giant Very big. Many dinosaurs were *giant* animals.

▲ **Synonym:** huge.
gi•ant (JĪ uhnt) *adjective.*

glance To take a quick look. I *glanced* in the mirror.

▲ **Synonyms:** look, glimpse.
glance (GLANS) *verb,* **glanced, glancing.**

government The group of people in charge of ruling or managing a country, city, state or other place. We held an election for our class *government.*
gov•ern•ment (GUHV urn ment) *noun, plural* **governments.**

grandmother Your father's mother or your mother's mother. My *grandmother* lives in New York City.
grand•mother (GRAND muthh uhr) *noun, plural* **grandmothers.**

graph A drawing that shows the relationship between changing things. We made a *graph* that showed how much our puppy had grown.
graph (GRAF) *noun, plural* **graphs.**

Hh

half One of two pieces the same size. Dad sawed the board in *half* to make a bench.

▲ **Synonym:** part.
half (HAF) *noun, plural* **halves.**

Ha•waii•an (huh WĪ uhn)

history The story or record of what has happened in the past. That old house has an interesting *history*.

his•to•ry (HIS tuh ree) *noun*, *plural* **histories.**

Hmong (huh MAHNG)

homework Work that a teacher asks children to do at home. I can finish my *homework* before dinner. *Noun.*
▲ **Synonym:** schoolwork.
home•work (HOHM wurk)

honor **1.** Something given or done to show great respect. The hero received a medal and other *honors. Noun.* **2.** To show or feel great respect for a person or thing. The city *honored* the team with a parade. *Verb.*
▲ **Synonyms:** adore, regard.
hon•or (AHN uhr) *noun*, *plural* **honors;**
verb, **honored, honoring.**

hope **1.** To wish for something. I *hope* that you will feel better soon. *Verb.* **2.** A strong wish that a thing will happen. My *hope* is that you will win. *Noun.*
hope (HOHP) *verb,* **hoped, hoping;** *noun, plural* **hopes.**

hour **1.** A unit of time equal to 60 minutes. There are 24 *hours* in a day. **2.** A time of day. At what *hour* should we meet?
hour (OWR) *noun, plural* **hours.**

hundred Ten times ten. 100. She is a *hundred* years old.
hun•dred (HUHN drihd) *noun, plural* **hundreds;** *adjective.*

hurry To move fast. Let's *hurry* and clean up our room.
hur•ry (HUHR ee) *verb,* **hurried, hurrying.**

407

Ii

iceberg A very large piece of floating ice. The penguins lived on an *iceberg*.

    ice•berg (ĪS burg) *noun, plural* **icebergs.**

idea Something that you think of. We all had different *ideas* about what to name our pet turtle.

    i•de•a (ī DEE uh) *noun, plural* **ideas.**

important Having value or meaning; worth paying attention to. It is *important* to look both ways before crossing.

    im•por•tant (ihm POR tuhnt) *adjective.*

Jj

Jamaica (juh MAY kuh)

join 1. To come together. Where do the two rivers *join?* **2.** To become a member of. My brother plans to *join* the soccer team.

    join (JOYN) *verb,* **joined, joining.**

juggler A person who keeps balls or other objects in continuous motion by skillful tossing and catching. The *juggler* kept four oranges in the air.

    jug•gler (JUG luhr) *noun, plural* **jugglers.**

Ll

lariat A long rope with a loop at one end, used to catch animals. The rancher used a *lariat* to rope the calf.

    lar•i•at (LAR ee uht) *noun, plural* **lariats.**

lean 1. To bend; to be at a slant. She had to *lean* out the window to see. **2.** To rest or rely on a person or thing for support. The monkey *leaned* against the branch.
▲ **Synonyms:** bend, tip.
lean (LEEN) *verb,* **leaned, leaning.**

lei A traditional Hawaiian wreath of flowers, leaves, or other material worn around the neck. When we got off the plane in Hawaii, each of us was given a *lei*.
lei (LAY) *noun, plural* **leis.**

lesson Something to be learned, taught, or studied. Today's math *lesson* was on subtraction.
les•son (LES uhn) *noun, plural* **lessons.**

library A room or a building where books are kept. People can use the books in the *library* or borrow them to take home.
li•brar•y (LĪ brair ee) *noun, plural* **libraries.**

life A way of living.
life (LĪF) *noun, plural* **lives.**

limit The point at which something must end. There was a *limit* on how much candy we could take.
lim•it (LIHM iht) *noun, plural* **limits.**

lonely Unhappy about being alone. Gabe is *lonely* because all his friends are away.
▲ **Synonyms:** alone, solitary.
lone•ly (LOHN lee) *adjective,* **lonelier, loneliest.**

lucky Having good things happen. I was *lucky* to have won.
luck•y (LUK ee) *adjective,* **luckier, luckiest.**

Mm

Maurice (maw REES)

melt To change from being hard or solid into being soft or liquid. The ice-cream cone *melted* in the sun.
melt (MELT) *verb,* **melted, melting.**

memory 1. The ability to remember things. Aunt Mimi has a good *memory* for dates and never forgets anyone's birthday. 2. A person or thing that is remembered. My summer in camp is one of my happiest *memories.*
mem•o•ry (MEM uh ree) *noun, plural* **memories.**

message Words or information sent from one person to another. I left a *message* for them to call me when they got home.
mes•sage (MES ij) *noun, plural* **messages.**

mochila A saddle covering made of hide or leather. *Mochilas* with pockets were used by Pony Express riders.
mo•chi•la (moh CHEE luh) *noun, plural* **mochilas.**

model A small-sized copy of something. They made a *model* of a castle.
mod•el (MOD uhl) *noun, plural* **models.**

mountain A very high mass of land. Some people go skiing in the *mountains* for vacation.
▲ Synonyms: hill, peak.
moun•tain (MOWN tuhn) *noun, plural* **mountains.**

mustang A wild horse that lives on the American plains; a bronco. The *mustangs* galloped across the prairie.

    mus•tang (MUS tang) *noun, plural* **mustangs.**

notice To see or pay attention to something. Erin *noticed* a rabbit hiding in the bushes.

    no•tice (NOH tis) *verb,* **noticed, noticing.**

Oo

order 1. The way in which things are arranged; position. We stood in *order* from oldest to youngest. **2.** Clean or neat condition. Please keep your room in *order. Noun.* **3.** To tell to do something; to command. The police officer *ordered* us to sit. *Verb.*

    or•der (OR duhr) *noun, plural* **orders;** *verb,* **ordered, ordering.**

Pp

parent A mother or a father. My *parents* took us skating.

    par•ent (PAIR uhnt) *noun, plural* **parents.**

parrot A bird with a wide, curved bill, a long, pointed tail, and brightly colored feathers. Amy's pet *parrot* squawked .

    par•rot (PAR uht) *noun, plural* **parrots.**

pasture A field where animals graze. We saw sheep grazing in the *pasture.*

    pas•ture (PAS chuhr) *noun, plural* **pastures.**

411

penguin A bird whose feathers are black or gray on the back and white on the front. Penguins cannot fly. Their wings look like flippers and are used for swimming. Most penguins live in or near Antarctica. The *penguin* swam toward the iceberg.

pen•guin (PEN gwin *or* PENG gwin) *noun, plural* **penguins.**

peppermint A candy that is flavored with peppermint oil, made from the leaves of mint plants. The *peppermint* made my breath taste fresh.

pep•per•mint (PEP uhr mint) *noun, plural* **peppermints.**

pheasant A large bird that has a long tail and brightly colored feathers.

pheas•ant (FEZ uhnt) *noun, plural* **pheasants.**

planet Any one of the nine large bodies that revolve around the sun, including Earth. The astronauts safely landed on *planet* Earth.

plan•et (PLAN it) *noun, plural* **planets.**

pocket A small bag or pouch that is sewn into a garment, suitcase, or purse. *Pockets* are for holding coins and other small things.

pock•et (POK iht) *noun, plural* **pockets.**

pour To make a liquid flow from one container to another. Dad *poured* soup into our bowls.

pour (POR) *verb,* **poured, pouring.**

president The leader of a group of people. We are going to have an election to choose the *president* of our class next week.
pres•i•dent (PREZ uh duhnt) *noun, plural* **presidents.**

promise To say that you will be sure to do something. Andy *promised* to keep my secret.
prom•ise (PROM ihs) *verb,* **promised, promising.**

proud Feeling good about something you have done. Ron was *proud* of the card he made for his mother's birthday.
proud (PROWD) *adjective,* **prouder, proudest.**

Qq

quail A bird that has a plump body and brown or gray feathers often dotted with white.
quail (KWAYL) *noun, plural* **quail** or **quails.**

Rr

record **1.** An act that is better than all others of its kind. The runner set a new *record* for the race. **2.** A written account. The school keeps a *record* of each student's attendance. *Noun.* **3.** To set down in writing. *Verb.*
re•cord (REK uhrd) *noun, plural* **records.** (rih KORD) *verb,* **recorded, recording.**

remember To think of something again, or still. I will always *remember* my first puppy.
re•mem•ber (rih MEM buhr) *verb,* **remembered, remembering.**

413

repair To fix or mend something. We *repaired* the broken leg of the table.

    re•pair (rih PAIR) *verb,* **repaired, repairing.**

repeat To do or say something again. The teacher asked me to *repeat* my answer because he could not hear me.

    re•peat (rih PEET) *verb,* **repeated, repeating.**

rule 1. A direction that tells what you can and cannot do. One of the *rules* at school is that you cannot run in the halls. *Noun.* **2.** To lead. The queen *ruled* her country well. *Verb.*

    rule (ROOL) *noun, plural* **rules;** *verb,* **ruled, ruling.**

rush 1. To move, go, or come quickly. We *rushed* so we wouldn't be late. *Verb.* **2.** A busy or hurried state. We were in a *rush* to get to the show on time. *Noun.*

    rush (RUSH) *verb,* **rushed, rushing;** *noun, plural* **rushes.**

saddle 1. A seat for a rider on the back of a horse or similar animal. A saddle is usually made of leather. The rider sat tall in the *saddle. Noun.* **2.** To put a saddle on. The cowhand *saddled* the horse. *Verb.*

    sad•dle (SAD uhl) *noun, plural* **saddles;** *verb,* **saddled, saddling.**

safety Freedom from harm or danger. The police work for the *safety* of us all.

    ▲ **Synonyms:** protection, security.

    safe•ty (SAYF tee) *noun.*

seal A mammal that lives in coastal waters and has flippers instead of feet. The *seal* on the iceberg made a barking sound.
seal (sihl) *noun, plural* **seals.**

search To look carefully for something. Dad had to *search* the house for his keys.
▲ **Synonyms:** seek, hunt.
search (SURCH) *verb,* **searched, searching.**

serious 1. Important. Not paying attention in school is a *serious* matter. **2.** Not joking. Were you *serious* about taking piano lessons?
se•ri•ous (SIHR ee uhs) *adjective.*

Shao (SHOW)

shy 1. Not comfortable around people; bashful. The *shy* child wouldn't come into the room. **2.** Easily frightened; timid. Some animals are *shy* around people.
shy (SHĪ) adjective, **shyer** or **shier, shyest** or **shiest.**

special Not like anything else; important. Your birthday is a *special* day. Juan is a *special* friend of mine.
▲ **Synonym:** unique.
spe•cial (SPESH uhl) *adjective.*

squeeze 1. To press hard. *Squeeze* the tube of toothpaste from the bottom. **2.** To get by squeezing or applying pressure. I *squeezed* the juice from an orange.
squeeze (SKWEEZ) *verb,* **squeezed, squeezing.**

415

stagecoach A large, closed carriage pulled by horses, once used for carrying passengers, mail, and baggage. The *stage-coach* slowly bounced over the bumpy road.

> **stage•coach** (STAYJ kohch) *noun, plural* **stagecoaches.**

stampede 1. A sudden, wild running of a herd of animals. The storm frightened the cattle and caused a *stampede. Noun.* 2. To make a sudden, wild rush. The horses *stampeded* when they heard the helicopter overhead. *Verb.*

> **stam•pede** (stam PEED) *noun, plural* **stampedes;** *verb,* **stampeded, stampeding.**

statue A likeness of a person, animal, or thing made of stone, bronze, or clay. The museum had *statues* from ancient Greece.

> **stat•ue** (STACH oo) *noun, plural* **statues.**

stegosaurus A dinosaur that had bony plates sticking up along its backbone. It ate only plants and walked on all four feet. We saw a *stegosaurus* skeleton at the museum.

> **steg•o•sau•rus** (steg uh SOHR uhs) *noun, plural* **stegosauri** (steg uh SOHR ī)

success 1. A result that has been hoped for. The coach was pleased with the team's *success.*
▲ **Synonym:** achievement.
2. A person or thing that does or goes well. The party was a big *success.*
suc•cess (suhk SES) *noun, plural* **successes.**

Tt

telegraph A system for sending messages in code over long distances by means of electricity. She sent the important message by *telegraph*.
>**tel•e•graph** (TEL uh graf) *noun, plural* **telegraphs.**

tern A web-footed seabird similar to a gull. We saw a *tern* fly over the ocean.
>**tern** (TURN) *noun, plural* **terns.**

tornado A powerful wind storm with funnel-shaped clouds. A *tornado* can cause great destruction.
>**tor•na•do** (tor NAY doh) *noun, plural* **tornadoes** or **tornados.**

trick-or-treat (TRIHK or treet)

trouble 1. A difficult or dangerous situation. The town will be in *trouble* if the dam breaks. *Noun.* **2.** Extra work or effort. We all went to a lot of *trouble* to throw the party. *Noun.* **3.** To disturb. May I *trouble* you for a glass of water? *Verb.*
>**trou•ble** (TRUB uhl) *noun, plural* **troubles;** *verb,* **troubled, troubling.**

truce A short halt in fighting, agreed to by both sides, who then try to make peace. Let's declare a *truce* so we can finish our game.
>**truce** (TROOS) *noun, plural* **truces.**

Tutu (TOO TOO)

Uu

understand To get the meaning of; to know. I didn't *understand* the teacher's question.
un•der•stand (un duhr STAND) *verb,* **understood, understanding.**

Vv

vaquero A cowboy, especially of Mexico, South America, or the southwestern United States.
va•que•ro (va KAIR oh) *noun, plural* **vaqueros.**

visit 1. To go to see. We *visited* them last Sunday. *Verb.* **2.** A short stay or call. We paid a *visit* to my old friend. *Noun.*
vis•it (VIZ it) *verb,* **visited, visiting;** *noun, plural,* **visits.**

Ww

weigh 1. To have an amount of heaviness. I *weigh* 60 pounds. **2.** To find out how heavy something is. I *weighed* myself.
weigh (WAY) *verb,* **weighed, weighing.**

whisper 1. To speak in a very quiet voice. The teacher asked the children to stop *whispering. Verb.* **2.** A soft way of speaking. Grace heard *whispers* in the movie theater. *Noun.*
▲ **Synonym:** murmur.
whis•per (WHIS puhr) *verb,* **whispered, whispering;** *noun, plural* **whispers.**

wild Not controlled by people; living or growing naturally. There are *wild* animals living on the plains of Africa.

▲ **Synonyms:** free, untamed. **wild** (WĪLD) *adjective,* **wilder, wildest.**

wonderful Amazing, unusual, or very good. At the circus we all stared at the *wonderful* acrobats.

▲ **Synonyms:** marvelous, astonishing. **won•der•ful** (WUN duhr fuhl) *adjective.*

worry to feel a little afraid about something. Mom and Dad start to *worry* if we come home late from school.

▲ **Synonyms:** feel anxious, feel troubled. **wor•ry** (WUHR ee) *verb,* **worried, worrying.**

worth 1. Having the same value as. The old coin is *worth* thirty dollars. *preposition.*

2. The amount of money that something can be exchanged for; value. That jewel's *worth* was set at $50,000.

worth (WURTH) *preposition, noun.*

wriggle To twist or turn from side to side with short, quick movements; squirm. The snake *wriggled* in the grass.

wrig•gle (RIHG uhl) *verb,* **wriggled, wriggling.**

wrong Not right. His answer to the question was *wrong.*

▲ **Synonym:** incorrect. **wrong** (RONG) *adjective.*

419

ACKNOWLEDGMENTS

The publisher gratefully acknowledges permission to reprint the following copyrighted material:

"Arthur Writes a Story" by Marc Brown. From ARTHUR WRITES A STORY by Marc Brown. Copyright © 1996 by Marc Brown. Reprinted by permission of Little, Brown and Company.

"The Best Friends Club." This is the entire text and nineteen illustrations from THE BEST FRIENDS CLUB by Elizabeth Winthrop with illustrations by Martha Weston. Text copyright © 1989 by Elizabeth Winthrop. Illustrations copyright © 1989 by Martha Weston. Reprinted by permission of Lothrop, Lee and Shepard Books, a division of HarperCollins Publishers.

Text and art of "Best Wishes, Ed" from WINSTON, NEWTON, ELTON, AND ED by James Stevenson. Copyright © 1978 by James Stevenson. Reprinted by permission of Greenwillow Books, a division of HarperCollins Publishers.

"Cloud Dragon" by Pat Mora from CONFETTI: POEMS FOR CHILDREN. Text copyright © 1996 by Pat Mora. Reprinted by permission of Lee and Low Books, Inc.

"Doves" by Masahito, translated by Tzi-si Huang, from IN THE EYES OF THE CAT: JAPANESE POETRY FOR ALL SEASONS. Selected and illustrated by Demi. Copyright © 1992 by Demi. Reprinted by permission of Henry Holt and Company.

"Four Generations" by Mary Ann Hoberman from FATHERS, MOTHERS, SISTERS, BROTHERS: A COLLECTION OF FAMILY POEMS. Text copyright © 1991 by Mary Ann Hoberman. Illustrations copyright © 1991 by Marylin Hafner. By permission of Little, Brown & Company.

"Henry and Mudge" from HENRY AND MUDGE: THE FIRST BOOK by Cynthia Rylant, pictures by Suçie Stevenson. Text copyright © 1987 by Cynthia Rylant. Illustrations copyright © 1987 Suçie Stevenson. Reprinted by permission of Simon & Schuster Books for Young Readers.

JAMAICA TAG-ALONG. Text copyright © 1989 by Juanita Havill. Illustrations copyright © by Anne Sibley O'Brien. Reprinted by permission of Houghton Mifflin Company. All rights reserved.

"Lemonade for Sale" by Stuart J. Murphy. Text copyright © 1998 by Stuart J. Murphy. Illustrations copyright © 1998 by Tricia Tusa. Reprinted by permission of HarperCollins Children's Books, a division of HarperCollins Publishers.

"A Letter to Amy" is the entire work of A LETTER TO AMY by Ezra Jack Keats. Copyright © 1968 by Ezra Jack Keats. Reprinted by permission of HarperCollins Publishers.

"Luka's Quilt" by Georgia Guback. Copyright © 1994 by Georgia Guback, used by permission of HarperCollins Publishers. Reprinted by permission.

"The Merry-Go-Round" by Myra Cohn Livingston from A SONG I SANG TO YOU by Myra Cohn Livingston. Copyright © 1984, 1969, 1967, 1965, 1959, 1958 by Myra Cohn Livingston. Used by permission of Marian Reiner. "Morning Song" by Bobbie Katz from POEMS FOR SMALL FRIENDS by Bobbie Katz. Reprinted with copyright © 1989 Random House, Inc. permission of Bobbie Katz.

"Nine-in-One, Grr! Grr!" by Blia Xiong. Reprinted with permission of the publisher Children's Book Press, San Francisco, CA. Copyright © by Cathy Spagnoli. Illustrations copyright © 1989 by Nancy Horn.

"Time to Play" by Nikki Grimes from PASS IT ON: AFRICAN-AMERICAN POETRY FOR CHILDREN. Selected by Wade Hudson. Text copyright © 1991 by Nikki Grimes. Illustrations copyright © 1993 by Floyd Cooper. Reprinted by permission of the author.

Illustration
Bob Barner, 10-11; Holly Hannon, 12-13; Julia Gorton, 35, 55, 113, 123, 379; Liz Conrad, 36-37; James Ransome, 56-57; Claude Martinot, 91, 369; Sal Murdocca, 92-93; Karen Chandler, 94-109; Donna Perrone, 114-115; Kelly Sutherland, 124-125; Krystyna Stasiak, 126-127; Clare Schauman, 128-129; Andy Levine, 155, 191, 243, 253, 289, 319, 341; Michael Grejniec, 156-157; Vilma Ortiz-Dillon, 190, 214; David Galchult, 192-193; Myron Grossman, 215; Jo Ann Adinolfi, 216-217; Roger DeMuth, 244-245; Oscar Senn, 254-255; Gerardo Suzan, 256-257; Luisa D'Augusta, 258-259; Kathi Ember, 290-291; Roger Roth, 320-321; Kunio Hagio, 322-337; Dagmar Fehlau, 342-343; Miles Parnell, 403-404; John Carozza, 406, 419; Holly Johnes, 415.

Photography
5: b.r. Peter Yates/SABA; 7: b.r. David Doubilet; 9: b.r. FPG/Denine Cody; 14: b.l. Courtesy of Dorothy Donohue.. t.r. Courtesy of Connie Keremes; 32: Jay Brousseau/The Image Bank; 33: b. PhotoDisc; 88: b. Jake Wyman/Photonica/t. Jake Wyman/Photonica; 89 t. Corbis/Bob Krist/b. Jake Wyman/Photonica; 94: b. Courtesy of the artist/t. Courtesy of Angela Shelf Medearis; 110: t.l. PhotoDisc; 111: m.r. Ryan and Beyer/Tony Stone Images/t.r. PhotoDisc; 121: t.r. NASA; 130: b. Courtesy of HarperCollins Publishers; 152-153: b. PhotoDisc; 153: t. PhotoDisc; 189: b. PhotoDisc; 213: t. David Young-Wolff/PhotoEdit./b. Gary Faye/Photonica; 240-241: t. PhotoDisc; 241: b. PhotoDisc; 242. PhotoDisc; 250: Masterfile/(c) Kurt Amsler/. B. PhotoDisc; 251: b. David Doubilet; 260: t. (c) 1995 Rick Friedman. 287: PhotoDisc; 317: b. Joseph Van Os/The Image Bank; 318: PhotoDisc; 322: b. Courtesy of the artist; 338: b. Lawrence Migdale/Photo Researchers; 339: b. PhotoDisc; 340: b. PhotoDisc; 367: t. Westlight/Dow Hendren; 368: PhotoDisc; 376: t.l. Courtesy, US Mint; 395: c. Frank Whitney/The Image Bank/c.i. James Darell/Stone; 397: r.i. DiMaggio Kalish/Stock Market; 398: l. PhotoDisc; 400: Joao Silva/Black Star/PNI; 401: Alan Schein/The Stock Market; 402: Clay McBride/Nonstock/PNI; 405: Clive Boursnell/Tony Stone Images; 406: t.l. Ariel Skelley/The Stock Market; 408: Zefa Germany/The Stock Market; 409: Phil Kramer/The Stock Market; 410: Caroline Wood/Allstock/PNI; 411: Zefa Germany/The Stock Market; 412: Zefa Germany/The Stock Market; 413: Stuart Gilbert/Metropolitan Museum of Art, NY; 414: Ariel Skelley/The Stock Market; 416: Le Goy/Liaison International; 417: A & J Vekkajk/The Stock Market; 419: Tome Brakefield/The Stock Market.

Reading for Information
All photographs are by Macmillan/McGraw-Hill (MMH) and by Michael Groen for MMH except as noted below:

Table of Contents, pp. 382–383
Chess pieces, t.l., Wides + Hall/FPG; Earth, m.c.l., M. Burns/Picture Perfect; CD's, m.c.l., Michael Simpson/FPG; Newspapers, b.l., Craig Orsini/Index Stock/PictureQuest; Clock, t.c., Steve McAlister/The Image Bank; Kids circle, b.c., Daniel Pangbourne Media/FPG; Pencils, t.r., W. Cody/Corbis; Starfish, t.c., Darryl Torckler/Stone; Keys, c.r., Randy Faris/Corbis; Cells, b.r., Spike Walker/Stone; Stamps, t.r., Michael W. Thomas/Focus Group/PictureQuest; Books, c.r., Siede Preis/PhotoDisc; Sunflower, c.r., Jeff LePore/Natural Selection; Mouse, b.r., Andrew Hall/Stone; Apples, t.r., Siede Preis/PhotoDisc; Watermelons, b.r., Neil Beer/PhotoDisc; Butterfly, b.r., Stockbyte

386: b. J.A.Kraulis/Masterfile; 395: c. Stone; 395: b.r. PhotoDisc; 395: b.l. PhotoDisc; 396: c. Jacque Denzer Parker/Index; 396: c. CMCD/PhotoDisc; 397: c.i. DiMaggio Kalish/Stock Market; 397: l. Emma Lee/LifeFile/PhotoDisc